Complete EnglishSmart

Revised and Updated!

Grade 6

Grammar

Comprehension

Vocabulary

Writing

Usage

Copyright © 2012 Popular Book Company (Canada) Limited

All rights reserved. No part of this publication may be reproduced, stored in a retrieval system, or transmitted in any form or by any means, electronic, mechanical, photocopying, recording or otherwise, without the prior written permission of the Publisher, Popular Book Company (Canada) Limited.

Printed in China

ISBN: 978-1-897457-06-1

Complete EnglishSmart Contents

ISBN: 978-1-897457-06-1

ISBN: 978-1-897457-06-1

ISBN: 978-1-897457-06-1

ISBN: 978-1-897457-06-1

The Monarch Butterfly

The butterfly has long been a symbol of beauty. It has been around for nearly 50 million years. There are about 19,000 known species of butterflies. The Monarch butterfly is a member of the Danaidae family, which in turn is a member of Lepidoptera, the fourth largest order of insects. The Monarch is easily recognized by its reddish-brown wings, spotted with white dots and framed by a black border. It is commonly found in North America.

The metamorphosis and migration of the Monarch butterfly are two phenomena that make this insect one of the most interesting of all living creatures. In the caterpillar stage, the Monarch hangs upside down and sheds its outer skin. From within, the yellowish pupa finds a slit in the outer covering of the caterpillar and slowly increases the slit to emerge fully. The pupa is then transformed to a chrysalis state in which its skin becomes a hard capsule. Here it will remain to complete the transformation and emerge as a full-grown adult butterfly.

Although Monarchs live in the temperate climates of North America, they cannot endure the cold temperature consistent with seasonal changes. When the days get shorter and the air gets cooler, the Monarch instinctively prepares to migrate to a warmer climate. What is truly remarkable is the distance that these tiny, apparently fragile creatures can travel. Although there is a great deal yet to be learned about this mysterious migratory flight, it is known that the Monarch butterfly will travel up to 3,000 km one way to reach its winter roosts. Since the Monarch does not fly at night, it covers up to 130 km in a day. Favourite southern locations for the Monarch include Florida, California, and central Mexico.

ISBN: 978-1-897457-06-1

Recalling Details

A. Place "T" for true or "F" for false in the space provided for each statement.

1. There are nearly 19,000 species of butterflies. _____

2. Monarchs like to fly at night when it is cooler. _____

3. Monarchs can travel up to 130 km a day during migration. _____

4. The longest route a Monarch butterfly can make is 300 km. _____

5. Monarchs are recognized by their black wings with red spots. _____

6. A favourite destination for the Monarch in winter is central Mexico. _____

7. The Monarch knows its time to migrate when the snow falls. _____

8. Butterflies must avoid the sun. _____

Further Responses

How did you do? Check your answers over again. There are 5 false answers above.

B. Give answers to the following questions in sentence form.

1. What is the great mystery surrounding the Monarch butterfly?

_____

_____

_____

2. Explain the metamorphosis (changes) that the Monarch butterfly goes through.

_____

_____

_____

ISBN: 978-1-897457-06-1

Unit 1

The Sentence and Its Parts

- The basic sentence is made of two parts: the **Subject** and the **Predicate**.
- The **Subject** contains the bare subject (the doer of the action) and its modifiers such as adjectives and adjective phrases. The **Predicate** contains the verb and its modifiers such as adverbs and adverb phrases.
- The bare subject is usually a noun (a person, place, thing, or an idea) and the verb is usually an action word.

C. For each of the sentences below, draw a line separating the subject from the predicate. Underline the bare subject and put parentheses ( ) around the verb.

The subject may not always be a noun; it could be a verb form or an action word with an "ing" ending.

Example: The <u>boy</u> | (ran) all the way home.

The word "boy" is the bare subject. It is a noun (person) and the doer of the action.

The word "ran" is an action word and describes what the boy (subject) did.

1. The Monarch butterfly is a member of the Danaidae family.

2. The new watch failed to keep accurate time.

3. The cat chased the mouse around the living room.

4. The students assembled in the gymnasium for a presentation.

5. Hard work often results in success.

6. The girl in a pink T-shirt and blue jeans is my sister.

7. John and Tom walked home from school together every day.

8. The man over there told me to give you this form.

9. Last Sunday, my parents and I dined at a French restaurant.

10. Riding in the car with the window open was his dog's favourite pastime.

ISBN: 978-1-897457-06-1

Compound Words

- A **Compound Word** is formed by combining individual words to create a new word. The new word has a definition that is a blend of the meanings of the combined words.

  Example: every + where = everywhere   and   out + side = outside

D. **Draw lines to match the words in Column A with the words in Column B to create compound words.**

Column A		Column B
1. fire	•	• work
2. mail	•	• way
3. type	•	• place
4. when	•	• storm
5. wild	•	• less
6. wind	•	• writer
7. home	•	• box
8. rain	•	• ever
9. drive	•	• mill
10. care	•	• life

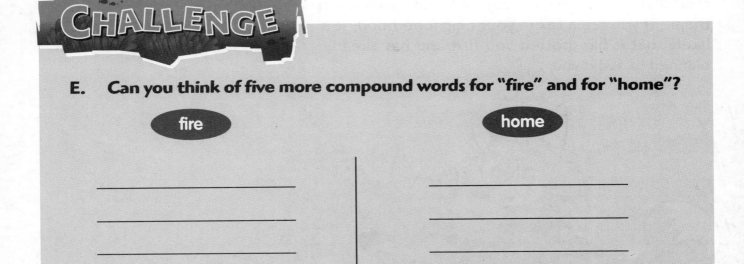

CHALLENGE

E. **Can you think of five more compound words for "fire" and for "home"?**

fire

home

_____

_____

_____

_____

_____

ISBN: 978-1-897457-06-1

Foxes, the New City Dwellers

Foxes are related to wolves and dogs and are found in most parts of the world. Typically, the fox hunts by night, but fox sightings on city streets in broad daylight are not uncommon. The red fox has been forced out of fast disappearing city ravines by inadequate food supplies brought on by the overpopulation of the species. The red fox has been seen hunting on golf courses, in neighbourhood backyards, and casually strolling residential streets in the heart of cities and towns.

Foxes are territorial and generally do not stray beyond a radius of 10 km. The home of a fox is called its earth but food shortage will drive a fox to expand its hunting area. The fox loves to eat rabbits, mice, and various rodents like squirrels but when its favourite prey is scarce, it will resort to wild fruit and grass.

The fox is an able hunter with its exceptional sense of smell, sight, and hearing. It also has excellent speed, reaching up to 50 km per hour. This speed, coupled with its cunning nature, has made the fox the traditional prey of the English fox hunt. During a hunt, foxes retrace their steps to throw off the scent of the pursuing hounds and subsequently, hide in trees as the hounds and the hunters speed by.

Foxes usually mate for life and live approximately 10 to 12 years. They mate in the middle of winter and produce between 2 and 8 cubs. Although foxes generally stay clear of human beings, it is advisable not to approach them. If you see a fox in your neighbourhood, it is likely that it has spotted you first and has already planned to avoid you.

ISBN: 978-1-897457-06-1

Skimming for Information

- When we skim for instant information, we read a passage quickly looking for the answers to factual questions.

A. **Read each question and skim immediately to find the answer. Write the brief answer in the space provided.**

1. To which other animal groups are foxes related? _____

2. At what time of day does a fox usually hunt? _____

3. Which kind of fox is seen most often in the city? _____

4. What is the radius of a fox's territory? _____

5. What is the term used for a fox home? _____

6. What animals does a fox like to eat? _____

7. How long is a fox expected to live? _____

8. How fast can a fox run? _____

9. When animals are not available to eat, what will the fox turn to for food?

_____

10. How does a fox throw off the pursuing dogs during a fox hunt?

_____

Summarizing

B. **In your own words, explain how the fox has adapted to change.**

_____

_____

_____

_____

_____

ISBN: 978-1-897457-06-1

The Noun as Object

- **Noun as Object of the Verb:** The object of a verb is the receiver of the action of the verb.

  Example: He placed the book in the drawer.

  The noun "book" is the object of the verb "placed". It is the object because it is what is being "placed".

- **Noun as Object of the Preposition:** The object of a preposition is the noun that follows the preposition in a phrase.

  Example: The girls of the sixth grade put on a play.

  The noun "grade" is the object of the preposition "of".

C. **Underline the nouns as objects. If they are objects of prepositions, circle the prepositions preceding them.**

1. The pianist played the piano for all the people.

2. He sat in the kitchen and ate the entire cake by himself.

3. He kicked the football through the goal posts.

4. The members of the team played hockey against another team.

5. He enjoyed the movie with the scary ending.

6. Get the ball before it goes on the road.

7. Of all of her friends, she liked Susan the best.

8. In the middle of the night, he woke up all the neighbours.

9. John and Anne were late for school.

10. Never before had he worried so much about his school grades.

11. Please put this box into the drawer.

12. He is thinking of an interesting title for his new book.

ISBN: 978-1-897457-06-1

Prefixes

- **Prefixes** are added to root words to alter their meanings. They often create words that are opposite.

  Example: *un + familiar = unfamiliar*

  In this case, when a prefix is added, it creates an opposite meaning or an antonym.

D. **Add the proper prefixes to the following words to create new words.**

1. appropriate (un, in)

   _____

2. view (re, de)

   _____

3. respect (un, dis)

   _____

4. dependable (in, un)

   _____

5. dependent (un, in)

   _____

6. form (re, un)

   _____

7. mature (in, im)

   _____

8. pleased (dis, un)

   _____

9. certain (in, un)

   _____

10. urban (im, sub)

    _____

11. reliable (un, in)

    _____

12. tasteful (dis, un)

    _____

13. common (dis, un)

    _____

14. tell (de, re)

    _____

15. regard (ir, dis)

    _____

16. belief (un, dis)

    _____

ISBN: 978-1-897457-06-1

When Wayne Gretzky was just six years old, his father, Walter Gretzky, managed to sign him to play with the ten-year-olds in the Atom League in Brantford, Ontario, giving him his first <u>opportunity</u> to play on a team. Mr. Gretzky was an <u>avid</u> hockey fan and excellent teacher. He made a rink in his backyard where he drilled Wayne on the basic skills and <u>instilled</u> in him the desire to practise hard and always give his all in every game.

Actually, Wayne was too young to play organized hockey. Being so small, he had difficulty controlling his <u>oversized</u> hockey sweater which was constantly getting in the way of his stick on his shooting side. To <u>compensate</u>, Wayne tucked in his jersey on the one side and consequently established his trademark style. Years later, thousands of young hockey players would be wearing their jerseys the same way <u>imitating</u> the Great One.

"The Great One" — Wayne Gretzky (1)

In his first season of organized hockey, Gretzky managed to score only one goal. However, in his second season, he scored 27, 104 in his third season, and an <u>astounding</u> 196 goals in the following season. By the time Wayne was ten, the proper age for his league, he had established himself as a <u>prodigy</u> by scoring an incredible 378 goals in a single season. As a young hockey player, Wayne's idol was Gordie Howe, the great Detroit Red Wings player, who held numerous scoring titles. Little did Wayne know at the time that he would go on to <u>shatter</u> all those records and set new ones that seem <u>insurmountable</u> today.

Gretzky made his professional <u>debut</u> in 1978 at the age of 18 with the Indianapolis Racers of the World Hockey League (WHA). The Racers fell into financial trouble and had to sell Gretzky to the Edmonton Oilers. In his first season with the Oilers, Wayne scored 43 goals and added 61 assists for a 72-game total of 104 points. When the WHA began to fall apart, the Edmonton Oilers were <u>incorporated</u> into the National Hockey League (NHL) for the 79'-80' season and, in this, his first official year in the NHL, Gretzky amassed 51 goals and 86 assists for a total of 137 points. He was voted the League's most valuable player – an honour he was to go on to achieve eight <u>consecutive</u> times.

During his years with the Oilers, Gretzky broke Phil Esposito's scoring record with 92 goals, <u>surpassing</u> the 200-point per season <u>milestone</u>. Later he established an all-time scoring record with 215 total points in a single season.

ISBN: 978-1-897457-06-1

Checking the Facts

A. Answer the following questions.

1. At what age did Gretzky first play organized hockey?

   _____

2. Who first taught Gretzky the game of hockey?

   _____

3. How old were Gretzky's teammates on his first organized team?

   _____

4. How many goals did Gretzky score in his first year of organized hockey?

   _____

5. Who was Gretzky's hockey idol when he was growing up?

   _____

6. How old was Gretzky when he signed his first professional contract?

   _____

7. How many points in a single season did Gretzky score to establish the all-time record?

   _____

Drawing Conclusions

B. Answer the questions in sentence form.

1. What skills did Gretzky possess that made him such a great player?

   _____

   _____

2. How did Walter Gretzky contribute to his son's success?

   _____

   _____

ISBN: 978-1-897457-06-1

Noun Clauses

- A **Noun Clause** acts as a noun in a sentence. It may act as subject or object of a verb, or object of a preposition.

Example 1: **Noun Clause as Subject of a Sentence**

Whoever wins the race will claim the prize.

The group of words "whoever wins the race" is a noun clause acting as subject.

Example 2: **Noun Clause as Object of a Verb**

The students didn't know where the meeting was.

It is "where the meeting was" that the students did not know; therefore, the noun clause "where the meeting was" is object of the verb "know".

Example 3: **Noun Clause as Object of a Preposition**

The teacher was pleased by how well the students were doing.

The word "by" is a preposition and "how well the students were doing" is a noun clause acting as object of the preposition.

C. **Underline the noun clauses and indicate in the spaces provided whether they are Subject (Subj.), Object (Obj.), or Object of a preposition (Obj. of prep.).**

1. We found where the Toyland was located. _____

2. I remembered what you told me to do. _____

3. The teacher was dissatisfied with what they did. _____

4. He asked that his name not be used. _____

5. Whatever choice is made will be fine. _____

6. Nobody told us how we could get to the destination. _____

7. We can judge our success by how we are rewarded. _____

8. What he had said in the meeting was reported in the news. _____

9. I don't know how I can avoid the problem. _____

10. Don't bother me with what the program is about. _____

ISBN: 978-1-897457-06-1

Learning New Words in Context

- When we read unfamiliar words, it is useful to use the sentence in which these words appear to help us understand their meanings. The information given in the sentence and the purpose of the sentence is its context.

D. **Match the underlined words in the passage with their meanings.**

Read the sentence in which each underlined word appears. After you complete filling in the list, use your dictionary to check the meaning of each underlined word.

Meaning	**Underlined Word**
1. beginning, first time	
2. break into pieces	
3. make up for	
4. inspired, promoted	
5. very big, too large	
6. genius	
7. chance	
8. difficult to overcome	
9. keen	
10. all in a row	
11. joined, made part of	
12. overcoming, going beyond	
13. copying	
14. shocking	
15. accomplishment	

ISBN: 978-1-897457-06-1

After the 1989 Stanley Cup victory, Gretzky was traded by Edmonton to the Los Angeles Kings, a team with a <u>losing</u> record and very <u>few</u> spectators in attendance at home games. Los Angeles was a great baseball city and the game of hockey was foreign to the people there. It was not long, however, until the citizens of Los Angeles came out to witness the greatest player to <u>ever</u> play the game. Gretzky did not disappoint them. In 1989 he broke Gordie Howe's lifetime scoring record of 1,850 total points and went on to lead the Kings to the Stanley Cup finals. The once sparsely occupied arena in Los Angeles was then sold out for every home game as the Kings' fans embraced Gretzky.

Gretzky states in his autobiography: "The greatest game of my life might not have been a hockey game. It might have been a Celtics–Lakers game." Gretzky was in attendance at that basketball game when a beautiful young lady came over to say hello. That was the moment when Wayne met his <u>future</u> wife Janet Jones, a dancer, model, and movie actress.

Gretzky has <u>always</u> exhibited respect for fellow NHL players and expressed admiration for past hockey greats. He <u>openly</u> praised the accomplishments of Gordie Howe and Jean Belliveau. He had the greatest respect for Mario Lemieux, the player thought most likely to break his scoring titles, and, of course, for his other best friend, Mark Messier. In his autobiography, Gretzky closes by listing the five players he would choose as his <u>personal</u> All-Star Team. In goal, he put Grant Furr and on the defense, he put Larry Robinson and Paul Coffey. His choice for forwards were Gordie Howe and Mark Messier, and at centre he placed Mario Lemieux.

"The Great One" — Wayne Gretzky (2)

Gretzky was not very big in stature, nor was he particularly fast on skates. He did, however, have the <u>uncanny</u> ability to control the offence of the game. <u>Pinpoint</u> passing, the knack for finding his teammates, and the creativity to mastermind scoring opportunities virtually every shift on the ice account for his <u>total</u> domination of the game of hockey. When Gretzky retired in 1999, fans were saddened at the prospect that such a great player and ambassador of the game would never play again.

18

ISBN: 978-1-897457-06-1

The Main Idea of a Paragraph

A. In sentence form, give a summary of the main idea of each paragraph. Keep your summary to only one sentence.

Paragraph One

_____

_____

Paragraph Two

_____

_____

Paragraph Three

_____

_____

Paragraph Four

_____

_____

Making Assumptions

B. Write "agree" or "disagree" in the space following each statement. Could you support your opinion with proof from the passage?

1. Fans will support a winning team. _____

2. There are many great players both past and present
    in the NHL. _____

3. Skill is more important than size. _____

4. Gretzky is a humble individual. _____

5. Any player, regardless of how great, can be traded. _____

6. Gretzky will always be remembered. _____

ISBN: 978-1-897457-06-1

Adjectives and Adverbs

- An **Adjective** modifies or describes a noun. It is usually placed next to the noun in a sentence. An **Adverb** modifies or describes the action of the verb.
- In the sentence, "The tall boy ran quickly", "tall" is an adjective that describes the noun (subject) of the sentence, "boy"; "quickly" is an adverb describing how the boy ran (verb).

C. Write if the underlined words are adjectives (adj.) or adverbs (adv.).

1. The <u>tall</u> building rose <u>majestically</u> up to the <u>blue</u> sky. _____ _____ _____

2. A <u>hockey</u> player must skate <u>quickly</u> during a game. _____ _____

3. The <u>teenage</u> girls ate lunch in a <u>local</u> restaurant. _____ _____

4. It was a <u>rainy</u> day when the <u>school</u> picnic began. _____ _____

5. The <u>tiny</u> dog barked <u>ferociously</u>. _____ _____

6. He was a <u>lucky</u> boy who was <u>always</u> on a <u>winning</u> team. _____ _____ _____

7. The <u>howling</u> wind thrashed <u>viciously</u> across the <u>corn</u> field. _____ _____ _____

8. The <u>recreation</u> centre had an <u>Olympic-sized</u> <u>swimming</u> pool. _____ _____ _____

> Adverbs often end in "ly"; sometimes nouns can act as adjectives.

D. Read the underlined words in the passage to see whether they are adjectives or adverbs. Write them below, and beside them write "adj." or "adv.".

1. _____ _____   2. _____ _____

3. _____ _____   4. _____ _____

5. _____ _____   6. _____ _____

7. _____ _____   8. _____ _____

9. _____ _____   10. _____ _____

ISBN: 978-1-897457-06-1

New Words

E. Below is a list of new words from the passage. Solve the crossword puzzle using the clues to the meanings of the words.

Word List

embraced   knack
autobiography   foreign
domination   witness
exhibited   ambassador
disappoint   stature
sparsely   uncanny

Try to figure out the meanings by reading the sentences in which these words appear. Not all of the words appear in the puzzle.

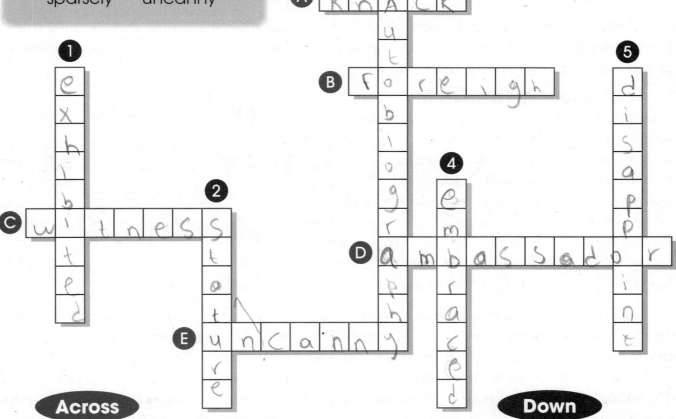

Across

A. Ability to do
B. From another land
C. See it happen
D. Representative
E. Odd, unusual

Down

1. Shown
2. Physical size
3. Story about self
4. Held tightly
5. Let someone down

Johannes Gutenberg was chosen to be the most important figure of the past millennium by the media. You may not be familiar with him but he has definitely influenced your life to some extent. Gutenberg is credited with inventing the printing press and consequently paving the way for printing books.

He was born into a noble family in the city of Mainz, Germany. His early training was in goldsmithing. In 1428, he moved to Strasbourg and lived there for over 20 years. It was in Strasbourg that he probably made his first experiments with movable type.

Johannes Gutenberg – the Pioneer of the Printing Press

Gutenberg utilized techniques of metalwork, such as casting, punch cutting, and stamping for the mass production of books. In those days, books in Europe were handwritten by scribes in a Gothic script with many flourishes and ligatures (interconnected letter pairs). To reproduce this "look", Gutenberg fashioned a font of over 300 characters, far larger than the fonts of today. To make this possible, he invented the variable-width mold and perfected the blend of lead, antimony, and tin used by type foundries up to the present century.

By 1450, Gutenberg was back in Mainz at work on a printing press. Between 1450 and 1455, while preparing to produce a large folio Latin Bible, Gutenberg is thought to have printed a number of smaller books, a calendar, and a papal Letter of Indulgence. The Bible of 42 Lines, the oldest surviving printed book in the Western world, was completed by August 15, 1456, and while it is now credited to Gutenberg, he appears to have been relieved of his supervisory position and his press before the time of its publication. Ironically, no printed material was ever credited to Gutenberg during his lifetime.

The discovery of the modern printing press changed the way information was delivered. In fact, this invention was responsible for educating the masses worldwide. Even today in the computer age, we rely heavily on the printed word or text for instruction, information, and for the pleasure of reading literature.

ISBN: 978-1-897457-06-1

Reading for Details and Making Assumptions

A. **Underline what you think is the best answer for each question.**

1. Why was the printing press such an important invention?

   Books could be printed.   It saved paper.   The Bible was printed.

2. What was Gutenberg trained as?

   metalworker   goldsmith   writer
   graphic artist

3. What type of family were the Gutenbergs?

   poor family   wealthy family   large family
   small family

4. What did Gutenberg first experiment with?

   movable type   new fonts   a new kind of paper
   writing books

5. Where did Gutenberg begin his first experiments?

   Mainz   Berlin   Strasbourg
   Vienna

6. What techniques did Gutenberg use for the mass production of books?

   goldsmithing   metalwork   blacksmithing
   plumbing

7. When was the first Bible completed?

   1656   1428   1456   1450   1455

8. How many characters were there in Gutenberg's font?

   200   300   400   100   500

9. Why were no printed materials ever credited to Gutenberg while he was alive?

   He didn't finish any books.   He was relieved of his duty.
   He died suddenly.

ISBN: 978-1-897457-06-1

Adjective and Adverb Phrases

- A **Phrase** is a group of words that has no subject or predicate and is often introduced by a preposition. A preposition is a "connecting" word that connects a noun or pronoun to some other words in a sentence.

  Here are some examples of prepositions:

  of, in, through, under, over, within, with, into, for, on, among, between, at, beside, besides, behind, from

- **Adjective Phrases** describe nouns and **Adverb Phrases** describe verbs.

  Example: The boys <u>on the team</u> practised <u>in the morning</u>.

  In the above sentence, there are two phrases: "on the team" and "in the morning". "On the team" describes the noun "boys" while "in the morning" describes the verb. "On the team" explains <u>who</u> the boys are and "in the morning" describes <u>when</u> they practised.

B.   For each sentence below, underline the phrase and in the space provided, state whether the phrase is adjective (adj.) or adverb (adv.).

> Adverb phrases often answer the questions "where" and "when".

1. She walked into the classroom late.   _____

2. The computer was set up for playing games.   _____

3. The girls from the private school wore school uniforms.   _____

4. The Bells of St. Mary's is a favourite Christmas film.   _____

5. The parcels in the car were birthday presents.   _____

6. The boy sat in the back seat.   _____

7. The dogs play in the yard.   _____

8. The kitten hid under the couch.   _____

C.   List the prepositions used in the above sentences.

1. _____   2. _____   3. _____   4. _____

5. _____   6. _____   7. _____   8. _____

ISBN: 978-1-897457-06-1

Suffixes

- **Suffixes** are added to root words to alter their meanings. They change the part of speech of root words, that is, how the root words are used in sentences.

  Examples: 1. retire ➜ retirement

  The root word "retire" is a verb but the new word "retirement" formed by adding the suffix "ment" is a noun.

  2. live ➜ lively

  The root word "live" is a verb but the new word "lively" formed by adding the suffix "ly" is an adjective.

D. Add the proper suffixes to the following words to create new words.

1. wicked (ment, ly)

   _____

2. simple (ent, ly)

   _____

3. pure (ance, ly)

   _____

4. confine (ly, ment)

   _____

5. glory (ment, ous)

   _____

6. treachery (ly, ous)

   _____

7. definite (ment, ly)

   _____

8. discover (ment, y)

   _____

9. invent (ion, ment)

   _____

10. heavy (ly, ous)

    _____

11. happy (ment, ness)

    _____

12. perform (ent, ance)

    _____

13. create (ive, ous)

    _____

14. major (ity, ion)

    _____

15. real (ity, ous)

    _____

16. anchor (ment, age)

    _____

Use your dictionary to check the spellings of the new words formed above.

25

ISBN: 978-1-897457-06-1

Left Brain, Right Brain

Did you know that your brain is divided into two halves: left and right? Scientists refer to these divisions as hemispheres. Each of these hemispheres (halves) controls different functions. In the majority of people, the left side of the brain controls fine motor activities on the right side of the body, which would account for the fact that most people are right-handed. The left side is also credited with controlling speech, the details of touch, and close vision in most people. The right side of the brain performs its own set of unique functions. You have been using the right side of your brain when you can tell if someone is happy or angry by his or her face or voice.

The specialized functions of the left and right sides of the brain are called lateralization. It is the functions of these sides of the brain that determine whether or not you favour the use of your right hand, foot, eye, or ear. Researchers are very interested in studying how we perform simple tasks and why the two hemispheres of the brain work differently. They hope to understand further how the brain processes information and relays information to the body which enables us to perform tasks.

Try a simple experiment to determine how your own brain processes information. Choose a stationary object on a wall on the other side of the room. Hold up your thumb at arm's length and with both eyes open, locate the tip of your thumb under the object. Close your right eye. Did your thumb jump to the right? Now close your left eye. Did your thumb remain in place? Over half the population would see their thumb jump to the right. This means that your right eye is more tuned into your visual perception than your left eye. Less than 10% of the population will experience the opposite result. The remainder of the population will experience no movement at all.

Only about 12% of the world's population (or 1 person in 7) is left-handed. Survey your friends, family, and classmates to determine if the statistics hold true.

ISBN: 978-1-897457-06-1

Organizing Information

A. **Make a list in the chart below of the skills and activities common to each side of the brain.**

Left Brain	Right Brain

B. **Fill in the blanks with the appropriate words from the list below.**

> left   right   10%   hemispheres
> touch   12%   lateralization

The specialized functions of the left and right sides of the brain are called

1. _____ . Our brain is divided into two parts called

2. _____ . Only about 3. _____ of the

world's population is left-handed. After conducting the

experiment, you would find that less than 4. _____

of the people tested would not see the thumb jump to the right.

Details of 5. _____ are attributed to the left side

of the brain. If you can tell how a person feels by looking at the

expression on his or her face, you have probably used the

6. _____ side of your brain. Fine motor activities

like writing is attributed to the 7. _____ side of the

brain.

ISBN: 978-1-897457-06-1

 Subordinate Clauses

- Unlike a phrase, a clause is a group of words that has a subject and a predicate but may not be a complete sentence. A **Subordinate Clause** depends on a main clause (sentence) to express a thought clearly.

Example: If I have time, I will go shopping.

"If I have time" is a subordinate clause because when used on its own, it does not make sense and lacks information. If the subordinate clause was used alone, it would be a fragment.

C. **Circle the subordinate clause in each of the sentences below.**

1. The bell had rung before I arrived at school.

2. Whenever I exercise, I get cramps in my legs.

3. After I ran up the hill, I was out of breath.

4. I love my dog which, I got as a birthday gift.

5. Before the teacher gave us any clues, we got the correct answer.

6. He went home although it was still early.

7. Whenever he scored a goal, he waved his arms.

8. He waited until the sun set.

9. She cut the pizza into sixteen slices so that it could be shared.

10. You are not going to pass the test unless you start studying now.

11. Jason has been on the baseball team since he was twelve.

12. Now that everyone has gone, we can take a rest.

13. He has to stay up late because the project is due tomorrow.

14. While they were halfway through the game, it started to rain.

ISBN: 978-1-897457-06-1

 **Word Challenge**

D. For each case, unscramble the word to form a word from the passage. Use the clue in parentheses to help you.

1.  (different, special)

2.  (to do with sight)

3.  (to decide)

4.  (run a test)

5.  (all the people)

6. 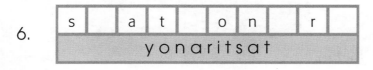 (remain in one spot)

7.  (view of something)

8.  (two halves)

9.  (left or right side)

ISBN: 978-1-897457-06-1

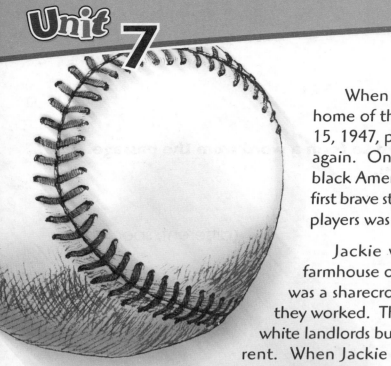

When Jackie Robinson trotted onto Ebbets Field, home of the Brooklyn Dodgers baseball team, on April 15, 1947, professional baseball would never be the same again. On that day, Jackie Robinson became the first black American to play major league baseball, and the first brave step in breaking the colour barrier against black players was boldly taken.

Jackie was born on January 31, 1919 in an old farmhouse on the outskirts of Cairo, Georgia. His father was a sharecropper. Sharecroppers never owned the land they worked. They were allowed to farm the land owned by white landlords but had to give half their crops to the owners as rent. When Jackie was only a year and a half old, his father abandoned the family, leaving Jackie's mother alone to care for the five children.

The Jackie Robinson Story (1)

Life for a black person showed no promise in the South, so Mrs. Robinson took her family to Pasadena, California in hopes of a better life. Jackie soon learned that being black in America was not easy. He was the subject of sneers and taunts from neighbours. Mrs. Robinson taught her children to be polite and stay out of trouble but also to be proud and stand up for themselves. Jackie never forgot these important lessons that would be invaluable to him later in life. Jackie, realizing that his mother had little money, helped out by doing odd jobs in the neighbourhood and turning over his earnings to his mother.

Jackie's first baseball was a rag ball – a ball of wool wrapped in a rag. He played with it all day long and tried hitting it with a stick and found that he was quite good at doing it. When Jackie entered high school, he was immediately recognized for his athletic ability. In addition to being a track and field star, he played varsity football, basketball, and of course baseball.

ISBN

Fact or Opinion

- A **Fact** is a statement that can be proven by the text of a story. An **Opinion** is a person's thoughts or feelings about a subject based on what he or she has read. While opinions may be logical, they are not factual.

A. **Indicate whether each statement is a fact or an opinion by placing "F" or "O" in the space provided.**

1. Jackie Robinson was a great baseball player. _____

2. The Robinson family was very poor. _____

3. Jackie's father was a sharecropper. _____

4. Jackie's father left them because he was tired of working. _____

5. Mrs. Robinson moved to California to start a better life. _____

6. The Robinson children were not afraid to stand up for their rights. _____

7. Jackie didn't have money for baseball equipment. _____

8. Jackie first practised baseball with a rag ball. _____

9. Jackie knew as a child that he could be a ball player. _____

10. The Robinson family had too many children to look after. _____

11. The day Robinson played professional baseball was the day the game changed forever. _____

12. Jackie was glad to give his mother the money he earned. _____

B. **Briefly answer the following question using the exact information from the passage to support your ideas.**

What difficulties in life did Jackie Robinson have to overcome as a youth?

_____

_____

_____

_____

ISBN: 978-1-897457-06-1

Sentence Sense

- A **Sentence** is a group of words that expresses a complete thought. When a sentence does not express a complete thought and leaves the reader wondering what comes next, or it is unfinished, it is called a fragment.

C. **Indicate whether each group of words below is a complete sentence or a fragment. Write "C" for a complete sentence and "F" for a fragment.**

1. The snake slid through the grass. _____

2. Jackie was quite good at hitting the rag ball. _____

3. The game covered in the sports section of the newspaper. _____

4. A long, long time ago. _____

5. I read the newspaper this morning. _____

6. Whenever I go to school. _____

7. Running quickly down the road. _____

8. All the students arrived at school in time. _____

9. The bus, which was scheduled to arrive at 4:00 p.m. _____

10. Mrs. Robinson moved to California with her family. _____

Writing Task

D. **Choose any four of the fragments above and add necessary words to make complete sentences.**

1. _____

2. _____

3. _____

4. _____

ISBN: 978-1-897457-06-1

Antonyms

- **Antonyms** are words that are opposite in meaning.
  Examples: love – hate; big – small; tall – short

E.   For each row of words, circle the antonym for the lead word.

1.	**vanish**	disappear	appear	show	illuminate
2.	**famous**	notorious	unknown	quiet	noisy
3.	**superb**	fair	natural	wonderful	poor
4.	**creative**	mindful	wise	dull	finicky
5.	**friendly**	happy	depressed	unsociable	naughty
6.	**rigid**	fixed	firm	flexible	tough

Prefix: "Anti"

- The **Prefix "Anti"** means "against", which, when added to a word, creates an antonym.

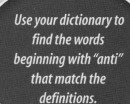

Use your dictionary to find the words beginning with "anti" that match the definitions.

F.   Fill in the blanks to form new words with the prefix "anti".

1.   creates immunity to fight disease   anti b ☐ ☐ y

2.   not friendly   anti s o ☐ ☐ a ☐

3.   cleans a wound   anti s e ☐ t ☐ ☐

4.   prevents car engine from freezing   anti f ☐ ☐ ☐ z ☐

5.   to defend against aircraft attacks   anti-a ☐ ☐ c ☐ ☐ f ☐

ISBN: 978-1-897457-06-1

In California, Robinson attended Pasadena Junior College where he set records in track and field, quarterbacked the football team, and led the basketball team in scoring. He led the Pasadena varsity baseball team to the championship and was voted MVP (Most Valuable Player). After graduation, Jackie was offered numerous scholarships to major universities. He chose UCLA, where he became an athletic hero. When he joined the Kansas City Monarchs of the Negro League, he was finally being paid to do what he did best.

The Jackie Robinson Story (2)

Professional baseball was a segregated sport. Black players were prohibited from playing. On August 28, 1945, that was about to change. Branch Rickey, a forward-thinking Dodger manager, signed Jackie Robinson to a contract and sent him to play for the Montreal Royals, a Dodger farm team. On April 10, 1947, history was made. Jackie became the first black American to sign a major league baseball contract.

When Jackie stepped onto New York's Ebbets Field that opening day, he faced the jeers of the crowd. The Dodgers won the game 5-3 and Jackie scored the winning run. Over the next few seasons, he was to endure racial insults, prejudicial treatment in public places, and death threats. One teammate even requested to be traded rather than play with Jackie. The St. Louis Cardinals threatened to cancel the scheduled league game with the Dodgers if Robinson played. Jackie answered the public scorn by winning the Rookie of the Year in 1947 and going on to help the Dodgers win six pennants in ten years. He stole home base, a particularly difficult task, an unprecedented 19 times.

Robinson retired in 1956 with a lifetime batting average of 0.311. It was not until 1959, however, that all major league teams fielded at least one black player. In 1962 he was inducted into the National League Hall of Fame – the first black player to receive that honour. He is remembered as a courageous man who single-handedly broke the colour barrier in professional baseball. Robinson died in 1972. His epitaph reads: "A life is not important except in the impact it has on other lives."

ISBN: 978-1-897457-06-1

Finding Important Information

A. **Write the exact sentence from the passage that most closely gives the information in each of the statements below.**

1. Jackie Robinson could play numerous sports well.

   _____

   _____

2. Jackie began to earn money as a professional baseball player.

   _____

   _____

3. One manager in professional baseball had different views from the rest.

   _____

   _____

4. Jackie endured racism against him and, by the end of the season, proved that he could play the game as well as anyone.

   _____

   _____

Reading into the Story

B. **Read the passage and write the answers.**

1. List three qualities of character that Robinson must have possessed that helped him overcome such adversity.

   a. _____ b. _____ c. _____

2. Give examples from the passage of actions or situations that prove the above answers.

   a. _____

   b. _____

   c. _____

ISBN: 978-1-897457-06-1

The Compound Sentence

- The **Compound Sentence** consists of two sentences that are related in topic or idea and are joined together. Each sentence could stand alone, but it is sometimes better to join them. A **Conjunction** is a little word that joins two independent sentences to form a compound sentence.

  Example: Jackie played many sports. Baseball was what he excelled in.

  Jackie played many sports <u>but</u> baseball was what he excelled in. "But" is the conjunction joining the two sentences.

C. **Write new sentences by joining the two sentences using "or", "but", or "and".**

1. Did she forget about the party? Was she sick?

    _____

2. The cat chased the birds. They flew away at once.

    _____

3. The storm lasted all night. We stayed awake.

    _____

4. He should hurry. He will be late.

    _____

5. Sometimes you win. Sometimes you lose.

    _____

6. The players tried hard. They lost the game anyway.

    _____

7. Some students went out for lunch. Others stayed at school.

    _____

8. You can't cure a cold. You can take medicine for relief.

    _____

9. You can buy the new game. You have to pay for it yourself.

    _____

ISBN: 978-1-897457-06-1

Homonyms

- **Homonyms** *are words that sound alike but have different meanings. Often these words are confused when we create sentences.*

D. **In each of the following sentences, circle the word that suits the meaning of the sentence.**

1. This was the first book that he had red, read this year.

2. A watt, what is a unit of measurement of electrical power.

3. He was a grate, great player in his time.

4. The boat was on sale, sail for a good price.

5. The driver did not break, brake in time.

6. The superstar accomplished another great feet, feat .

7. It never rains but it pores, pours .

8. She couldn't bear, bare to see the animal suffer.

E. **Write the homonym for each word in the puzzle. Use the meaning for the homonym as a clue.**

Word	Meaning for homonym
A. pier	to look at
B. border	pays to live in your house
C. sweets	another word for hotel rooms
1. core	a military term
2. swayed	a type of material
3. raise	given by the sun

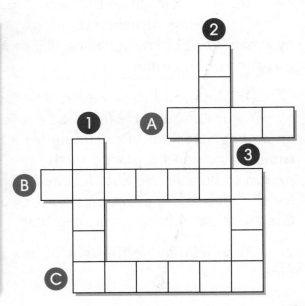

ISBN: 978-1-897457-06-1

Leonardo da Vinci is one of the most famous artists of all time. Immediately coming to mind at the mention of his name are the paintings of The Last Supper, John the Baptist, and the most renowned painting in the world, The Mona Lisa. However, da Vinci was not just a great painter; he was a visionary who drew sketches and plans for some of the great inventions of the future.

Concerned with a war raging with Venice, da Vinci designed a chariot with spear-like protrusions on each side to strike the enemy. He also sketched a drawing of an armoured car complete with wheels and a crank mechanism, arguably the first depiction of the modern-day tank.

Leonardo da Vinci –
Artist and Visionary

In da Vinci's time, Milan was filthy and overcome by a devastating plague. Da Vinci, disgusted with the conditions, designed a city with an elaborate sewage system complete with drainage. The lower level was also a place where horse stables could be housed. Da Vinci actually installed a similar design to work in Sforza Castle in Milan.

One of da Vinci's most interesting ideas was the design of a flying machine resembling a helicopter. First he designed a set of wings like those of a bird which could be attached to a man's arms. Then, he planned a machine that would feature two sets of wings attached to a long post propelled by a man sitting below pedalling. Once again da Vinci was ahead of his time.

Da Vinci had dreamed of the possibility of man working underwater. He designed a metal diving suit with an air bag attached. Protruding from the air bag was a tube that could be placed in the mouth, allowing the person to breath. He also designed web-like attachments for the feet to aid propulsion underwater and a waistband filled with air to keep a person afloat.

Da Vinci may be thought of as a man born out of his time.

Recalling Information

A. **Choose the correct option to complete each statement. Place a check mark beside your choice.**

1. Da Vinci designed a chariot because

   A. he was interested in new forms of transportation. _____

   B. he was worried about the war with Venice. _____

   C. this was a request from the Duke of Milan. _____

2. The most famous of da Vinci's paintings is

   A. The Last Supper. _____

   B. John The Baptist. _____

   C. The Mona Lisa. _____

3. Da Vinci designed a sewage system for the City of Milan because

   A. the city was filthy. _____

   B. the current system was not working properly. _____

   C. there was too much drainage. _____

4. The sewer da Vinci designed could also be used for

   A. housing. _____

   B. storage. _____

   C. stables. _____

5. Fascinated with flight, da Vinci designed

   A. a type of jet plane. _____

   B. a type of helicopter. _____

   C. a type of glider. _____

6. Da Vinci designed a metal diving suit for the purpose of

   A. man working underwater. _____

   B. catching fish. _____

   C. cleaning out the sewers. _____

ISBN: 978-1-897457-06-1

 The Complex Sentence

- The **Complex Sentence** has one main clause and one subordinate clause. A subordinate clause cannot stand alone. It depends on the main clause (sentence) for its complete meaning.

    Example: Complex sentence – When I walked home, it started to rain.
    Subordinate clause – when I walked home
    Main clause – It started to rain.

B.   Rewrite each pair of sentences below as a complex sentence.

Example: I ran quickly. I saw the dog. (when)

When I saw the dog, I ran quickly. / I ran quickly when I saw the dog.

1.   The boy fell off the swing. He was pushed. (because)

   _____

2.   The money was found. I looked everywhere. (after)

   _____

3.   The girls played in the yard. It was recess. (when)

   _____

4.   The tourists looked on. The farmer crossed the road with his sheep. (as)

   _____

5.   The team scored a goal. The fans cheered wildly. (whenever)

   _____

6.   It rained. My car was very clean. (before)

   _____

7.   The test was easy. She went over all her answers again. (although)

   _____

8.   The children were playing. Someone knocked on the door. (while)

   _____

ISBN: 978-1-897457-06-1

Developing New Words

C. **Use prefixes and suffixes to build new words from the root words. Write a synonym and an antonym for each of the root words.**

Root Word	New Word	Synonym	Antonym
1. create	creation	devise	destroy
2. develop			
3. curious			
4. decide			
5. form			
6. serious			
7. shout			
8. correct			
9. wonder			
10. slow			
11. collect			
12. hope			
13. pride			
14. please			
15. truth			
16. scholar			

Now that you have read the comprehension passages from the first nine units, let's see how well you remember them.

A. Place "T" (true) or "F" (false) beside each statement.

1. Our brains are divided into three sections – left brain, right brain, and middle brain. _____

2. Jackie Robinson first played for the Los Angeles Dodgers. _____

3. Gutenberg invented the printing press. _____

4. Wayne Gretzky retired in 1999. _____

5. The home of a fox is called an "earth". _____

6. First the Monarch butterfly becomes a chrysalis, and then a pupa. _____

7. Leonardo da Vinci is better known for his art than for his inventions. _____

8. Jackie Robinson was born in California. _____

9. Wayne Gretzky's father taught him how to play hockey. _____

10. A fox can reach a speed of 50 km per hour. _____

11. The oldest printed book of the Western world is the Bible. _____

12. Da Vinci was concerned with pollution. _____

13. Only 25% of the world's population is left-handed. _____

14. The specialized functions of the sides of the brain are referred to as hemispheres. _____

15. Gretzky retired before breaking Gordie Howe's scoring records. _____

ISBN: 978-1-897457-06-1

B. Circle the correct answers.

1. The Monarch butterfly is identified by

    A. black wings with red dots.   B. reddish brown wings with white dots.

    C. white wings with reddish brown dots.

2. Foxes stay close to home within a radius of

    A. 25 km.   B. 10 km.   C. 50 km.

3. Gretzky played his minor league hockey in

    A. Brantford, Ontario.   B. North Bay, Ontario.   C. Windsor, Ontario.

4. The player considered to be the most likely one to break Gretzky's records was

    A. Mark Messier.   B. Brett Hull.   C. Mario Lemieux.

5. Gutenberg, the inventor of the printing press, was born in

    A. Switzerland.   B. Germany.   C. Poland.

6. In most people, the left side of the brain controls

    A. emotions.   B. sight.   C. fine motor skills.

7. Jackie Robinson's father was a sharecropper which means

    A. he owned a business.   B. he worked on the fields he did not own.

    C. he owned a farm.

8. When Jackie Robinson stepped onto Ebbets Field to play his first professional game, the spectators

    A. greeted him warmly.   B. applauded.   C. jeered him.

9. Da Vinci's most famous painting is

    A. The Mona Lisa.   B. John the Baptist.   C. The Last Supper.

ISBN: 978-1-897457-06-1

Subjects and Verbs

The subject is the doer of the action; the verb is the action being done.

C. **Underline the bare subject and place parentheses ( ) around the verb of each sentence below.**

1. The train flew off the tracks.

2. Boys and girls played in the schoolyard.

3. In the forest, the animals slept.

4. The boy, after running as fast as he could, collapsed.

5. Many of the students were away from school due to illness.

Noun Clauses

D. **Place parentheses ( ) around the noun clause in each sentence below.**

A noun clause acts as a noun in a sentence and may be used as a subject or an object.

1. Whoever makes the decision will suffer the consequences.

2. He couldn't recall what the question was.

3. The story was written by whomever had the best information.

4. I was thinking about what you said last night.

5. How you figure out the answer to the math question is up to you.

Adjective and Adverb Phrases

Adjective and adverb phrases are groups of words that do the same job as adjectives and adverbs and are often introduced by a preposition.

E. **Underline the adjective phrase and place parentheses ( ) around the adverb phrase in each sentence below.**

1. The member of the team walked into the dressing room.

2. Students at the local school sold raffle tickets at the fair.

3. In all her years of teaching, she had never had such a nice class.

4. In the dark of night, the stranger from the crowd stepped forward.

ISBN: 978-1-897457-06-1

Complete Sentences and Sentence Fragments

F. Place "C" (complete) or "F" (fragment) after each sentence below.

A sentence is a complete thought while a sentence fragment is an incomplete thought.

1. Walking through the park. _____

2. Just up ahead, I saw a deer beside the road. _____

3. Wait until I catch my breath. _____

4. I remember my first bicycle. _____

5. Just when you think everything is going smoothly. _____

Compound and Complex Sentences

G. Place the word "compound" or "complex" after each sentence below.

A compound sentence has two principal clauses placed together. A complex sentence has a principal clause and at least one subordinate clause.

1. The students organized a baseball game and they played right through their lunch hour. _____

2. When the twilight has come, the boats rush to shore. _____

3. In the beginning, there was only the lower grade classes in the school, but the school soon expanded to include senior grades. _____

4. He hopped over the fence and the dog was waiting for him. _____

5. Keep your head up and watch for the ball. _____

6. If at first you don't succeed, try again. _____

7. Whenever the boy could not sleep, he read a book. _____

8. Before you leave, don't forget to close all the windows. _____

ISBN: 978-1-897457-06-1

Developing Vocabulary

Prefixes are added to the beginning of words and suffixes are added to the end of words to form new words.

H. Add the proper prefix to each word to make the opposite meaning.

1. possible   _____

2. spelled   _____

3. dependable   _____   4. mature   _____

5. necessary   _____   6. true   _____

I. Add the suffix in parentheses to each word and make the necessary changes.

1. possible (ity)   _____   2. simple (ly)   _____

3. attach (ment)   _____   4. glory (ous)   _____

5. treachery (ous)   _____   6. true (ly)   _____

Antonyms are words with opposite meanings.

J. Circle the best antonym for each word on the left.

1. **aware**	know	ignorant	adorn	attempt
2. **create**	make	find	search	destroy
3. **necessary**	appropriate	new	useless	tricky
4. **treacherous**	exciting	demanding	safe	dangerous
5. **gentle**	rough	smooth	calm	useful

ISBN: 978-1-897457-06-1

 **New Words**

K. **The following are some of the new words that you have learned. Draw a line to match each word with the definition.**

1.	person who is unusually talented	•
2.	things that happen one after another	•
3.	copy or mimic	•
4.	your first appearance	•
5.	go beyond what is expected	•
6.	pay a debt	•
7.	be enthusiastic	•

- A debut
- B imitate
- C prodigy
- D compensate
- E consecutive
- F avid
- G surpass

 Building New Words from Root Words

You may have to form a compound word.

L. **Make the necessary change in each root word to suit the definition.**

Example: attach – something added = attachment

1. suit – something to pack your clothes in = _____

2. correct – what you make in your notebook = _____

3. curious – something you have when you want to know = _____

4. proud – something you have when you are proud = _____

5. destroy – what there is when everything is destroyed = _____

6. joy – full of joy = _____

7. home – you take this home from school to work on = _____

8. fire – place to get warm = _____

9. use – when it offers no help = _____

10. know – when it is strange to you = _____

ISBN: 978-1-897457-06-1

Did you know that the record for the most straws put in someone's mouth is 151 or that the tallest person measures 8 feet 11 inches? Is it important to you to know that the oldest person ever lived to the age of 122? This information may appear useless but it was questions such as these that inspired the publication of the original *Guinness Book of Records* (now known as *Guinness World Records*), named after the renowned Irish brewery.

Guinness World *Records*

The Guinness Brewery dates back to 1759, when Arthur Guinness established the Guinness Brewery in Dublin, Ireland. In the early 1950s, the company director of the time, Sir Hugh Beaver, found himself involved, on more than one occasion, in arguing about trivial facts. It occurred to him that pub patrons everywhere were disputing facts on a variety of topics and that a book that could offer definitive answers to such arguments would be a useful reference. Also, he realized that such a book would be a great promotional idea, so he planned to publish it and make it available to pub licensees everywhere.

Beaver approached the McWhirter brothers, who owned a fact-finding company in London, to gather facts for what became *The Guinness Book of Records*. It took over a year of painstaking research to compile and verify the information and in 1955, the first copy, a 198-page edition, was published. It became an instant bestseller and the No. 1 selling book in Britain that year. *Guinness World Records* is now published in 100 countries in 24 languages with sales of over 100 million copies.

The fact that *The Simpsons* is the longest-running prime time animation television series and the most home runs hit in one professional baseball season is 73 may seem trivial; however, people worldwide crave the knowledge of such seemingly insignificant facts. Many an argument can be quickly resolved by simply referring to *Guinness World Records*.

ISBN: 978-1-897457-06-1

Recalling Details

A. **Fill in the blanks with the correct words from the answer list provided.**

| 100 | promotional | 1955 | 1759 | London |
| Dublin | 151 | 73 | licensees | Arthur |

1. The Guinness Brewery was founded in _____ .

2. The founder of the Guinness Brewery was _____ Guinness.

3. The McWhirter brothers were located in _____ .

4. The highest number of straws put in a human mouth is _____ .

5. The first copy of The Guinness Book of Records was printed in the year

   _____ .

6. The book was originally meant to be a _____ idea.

7. The Guinness Brewery is located in _____ .

8. Individuals who run a pub are called _____ .

9. Guinness World Records is published in _____ countries.

10. The record for home runs in the major leagues is _____ .

Opinion Based on Fact

B. **Recall details from the story to help you answer the following questions.**

1. Why did the Guinness Brewery think it was a good idea, even perhaps a necessity, to devise a book of facts?

   _____

   _____

2. Why do you think the book is so popular today?

   _____

   _____

ISBN: 978-1-897457-06-1

Compound–Complex Sentences

- A **Compound Sentence** is made up of two or more independent clauses. A **Complex Sentence** is made up of an independent clause with at least one dependent (subordinate) clause.
- A **Compound-Complex Sentence** is a combination of these two types of sentences.

    Example: Ryan has hearing problems. He has difficulty following the lessons. He often played truant.

    Compound-Complex Sentence:

    Because he has hearing problems, Ryan has difficulty following lessons and he often played truant.

C.   Rewrite the following paragraph using varied, interesting sentence structure.

Follow these steps:

- *Combine the sentences by creating compound, complex, or compound–complex sentences.*
- *Avoid repeating terms; use adjectives, adverbs, and phrases to replace sentences.*
- *Change short sentences to dependent clauses.*

The Annual Play Day

This year, our school play day was held on a Friday. Parents volunteered. Teachers volunteered. Parents, teachers, and some Grade 6 students planned the games and activities. The activities were fun. The play day began at 9:00 a.m. The play day ended at 4:00 p.m. Hundreds of children attended. Hundreds of children enjoyed the day very much. There was a bake sale. The clown blew up balloons. The clown handed the balloons to the children. The older students ran the games. The parents ran the bake sale. They raised lots of money.

_____

_____

_____

_____

ISBN: 978-1-897457-06-1

New Word Forms

- Adding suffixes to root words can create new words for different parts of speech.

  Examples: happy + ness becomes the noun "happiness"

  love + ly becomes the adjective "lovely"

  sweet + ly becomes the adverb "sweetly"

D. **Circle the words in the word search below that are formed from the root words in the list.**

delicate   sense   separate   sequence   repeat   reproduce

just   require   watch   volunteer   virtue   utility   willing   peace

r	d	w	a	t	c	h	f	u	l	l	y	p
w	f	s	e	p	a	r	a	t	i	o	n	r
s	r	e	p	e	t	i	t	i	v	e	d	o
x	e	q	e	r	t	n	a	l	i	v	e	d
v	p	u	a	u	w	j	o	i	r	o	l	a
b	r	e	c	b	a	u	e	z	t	l	i	c
n	o	n	e	m	n	s	t	a	u	u	c	t
j	d	t	f	o	s	t	r	t	o	n	a	i
k	u	i	u	t	u	i	s	i	u	t	c	e
t	c	a	l	w	v	c	v	o	s	a	y	n
l	t	l	l	q	t	e	n	n	r	r	b	p
h	i	s	y	s	e	n	s	o	r	y	c	t
k	o	r	e	q	u	i	s	i	t	i	o	n
s	n	u	n	w	i	l	l	i	n	g	l	y

ISBN: 978-1-897457-06-1

Unit 11

English – the Language of the World

It is believed that over a billion people (1/7 of the world's population) use English today and half of these have English as their mother tongue. Only Chinese surpasses English in individual use, but no language matches English in distribution. The rise of the English language to dominance is a remarkable story. When the Roman army, led by Julius Caesar, landed in England more than two thousand years ago, there was no English language. But a thousand years later, English was the native language of over 6 million Englishmen. English was then spread globally to all corners of the world by military personnel, travellers, the English, Irish, Scots, and Americans who represented business and political expansion.

Of the estimated 2,700 languages in existence in the world today, English has by far the most extensive vocabulary. The Oxford Dictionary lists half a million words while another half million technical and scientific terms, although not included in the dictionary, are widely used. By comparison, the German language has roughly 185,000 words while French uses only 100,000. English is now the language of business with over 80% of the world's telecommunications, faxes, and Internet correspondences in English.

The most significant development of the last 100 years is the use of English as a second language by over half a billion people in countries such as India and Holland. Political announcements and communications with the rest of the world promoting trade are often made in English, creating a link for non-English speaking countries with the Western world.

The desire for the world's population to learn to speak English has spawned numerous educational agencies that arrange for English language classes in Asian countries such as China, Japan, and Korea. With the dominance of English and six billion people worldwide as potential speakers of the language, the task of providing this education is daunting.

ISBN: 978-1-897457-06-1

Fact or Opinion

- A **Fact** is a statement that can be proven by referring directly to the text of the passage. An **Opinion** is a response the reader has to the information he or she gets from the passage. It may be based on fact, but is not factual.

A. Write "F" for fact or "O" for opinion in the space provided for each statement.

1. Eventually, everyone in the world will speak English. _____

2. Starting a school for the teaching of English is a good business idea. _____

3. Around the year 1000, over 6 million people were speaking English in England. _____

4. There are roughly 2,700 languages in the world today. _____

5. The Oxford Dictionary is the best source for learning the meaning of most English words. _____

6. If everyone spoke English, doing global business would be easier. _____

7. The English language spread all over the world by military personnel and travellers. _____

8. English is now the language of 80% of the world's communication. _____

Using Facts to Build Opinion

B. Use your own ideas to answer the questions. The information in the passage should help you develop a point of view.

1. Why is there suddenly a surge in the need to speak English all over the world?

    _____

    _____

2. What is the advantage of having most of the world speak English?

    _____

    _____

Punctuating Sentences

- A **Question Mark** follows a sentence that asks a question.
- An **Exclamation Mark** follows a sentence that makes an emphatic statement.
- A **Period** follows a sentence that makes a simple statement.

C. Place the appropriate punctuation mark for each sentence below.

1. Boy, that was a lot of fun
2. How many students take the bus to school
3. When I get home, I will have my dinner
4. Where is everyone going in such a hurry
5. Stop that nonsense immediately
6. How much gas we use depends on where we go
7. Look out for the car
8. Among all the children, who would like to share a pizza

Using the Comma

- The **Comma** has a variety of uses in a sentence.

  1. Use a comma to separate items in a list – He bought apples, oranges, pears, and grapes.
  2. Use a comma to separate a subordinate clause when the clause appears first in the sentence – Whenever I go to the beach, it seems to rain.
  3. Use a comma to set off a quotation – I asked, "When should I arrive?"
  4. Use a comma to set off words in apposition – John, the baker, makes wonderful cakes.

D. Add commas where necessary to the paragraph below.

The students the teachers and the parents attended the winter carnival. Although there was not very much snow there was a snow sculpturing contest. They ate hot dogs muffins and cakes and they enjoyed hot chocolate Coca-Cola and a variety of juices. The principal Mr. Johnson an avid skater showed off his skill at the rink. The grade eight students organized the games arranged the contests supervised the younger students and set up the signs. One student asked enthusiastically "Could we do this again next year?"

ISBN: 978-1-897457-06-1

Building New Words

E. **For each case, fill in the space with a new form of the word in parentheses to match the meaning of the sentence.**

Example: There were two _____ (divide) in the hockey league.

Change the word "divide" to form the new word "divisions" which suits the meaning of the sentence.

1. He will _____ (creative) a new piece of art for the display.

2. She was very _____ (population) with her classmates.

3. The _____ (script) on the trophy included his name.

4. She enjoyed the _____ (action) in talks with the group.

5. The _____ (gallop) horse sped by the racing fans.

6. _____ (tight) the lid to avoid spillage.

7. His desire to be famous was _____ (wish) thinking.

8. He bought the latest _____ (verse) of the computer game.

9. The _____ (success) businessman earned a high income.

10. The _____ (adventure) girl liked to climb mountains.

ISBN: 978-1-897457-06-1

No More Pencils ... No More Books

A familiar "end of year" chant for schoolchildren began with the words, "No more pencils, no more books". Could this also be a prophecy? Will the age of computer technology advance to the stage where books and pencils in schools become obsolete?

Before considering these questions, it is useful to reflect on the history of the computer. Its roots go back to 1822 when an Englishman by the name of Charles Babbage created a computation machine. Recognizing the need for storing information primarily mathematical in nature, Babbage attempted to develop a machine powered by a steam engine to store information on punch cards. Babbage's concept was sound but the technology available was inadequate to meet the task at hand.

The first electronic computer produced by the US Army in 1946 was named the ENIAC (electronic numerical integrator and calculator). It weighed 30 tons, and took up enough floor space to fill a normal-sized house. It was capable of performing about 5,000 operations per second but because it produced enormous amounts of heat while in operation, it had to be shut down regularly to cool off.

Advancements in computer technology can be recorded in four principal generations. The first would be the mainframe format such as the ENIAC. With the invention of the transistor, the second generation of smaller, faster, and less expensive computers came on the scene. By 1996, the miniature integrated circuits took the place of transistors, creating the new wave of computers with expanded memory capabilities, operating at relatively high speeds. Finally, the silicon chip marked the fourth generation of computers. These were smaller, faster, and cheaper initiating the beginning of the PC.

Imagine a school of the future where, instead of opening their textbooks, students would log on to a network on their laptops and download the lessons for the day. Assignments would be forwarded by e-mail after full revision and spell check. Perhaps, in the future, students simply log on at home and attend "virtual" school.

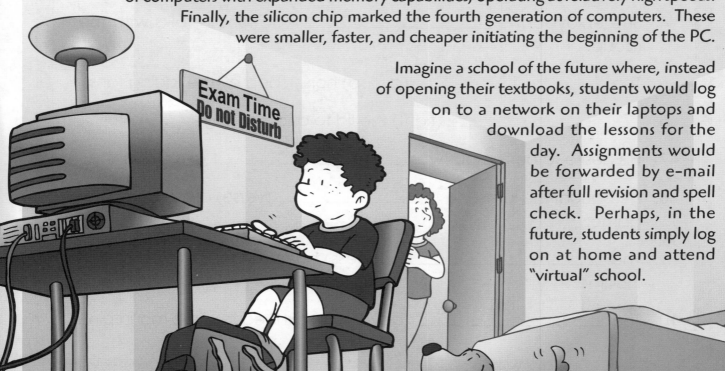

ISBN: 978-1-897457-06-1

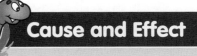

Cause and Effect

- A **Cause** is the reason why something happens. An **Effect** is what happens.
- An effect is the result of a cause and a cause results in an effect.

A. Write in the space provided either the cause or the effect for each statement.

1. Cause: _____

   _____

   Effect: Computers of the second generation were smaller, faster, and less expensive.

2. Cause: Miniature integrated circuits took the place of transistors.

   Effect: _____

   _____

3. Cause: _____

   _____

   Effect: Babbage created a computation machine.

4. Cause: The ENIAC produced enormous amounts of heat while in operation.

   Effect: _____

   _____

5. Cause: _____

   _____

   Effect: Babbage was unable to develop a steam-powered computer.

6. Cause: The fourth generation of computers used the silicon chip.

   Effect: _____

   _____

ISBN: 978-1-897457-06-1

Combining Sentences

- **Sentences** should contain a complete thought with descriptive details. A **Short Sentence** can be effective if it contains a singular idea that is best stated simply. Short sentences, particularly sentences with a common idea, should be combined to form longer and more interesting sentences.

- Sentences may be combined by using the following:
  a) subordinate clauses
  b) conjunctions
  c) semicolons

B. **Rewrite the following paragraph combining sentences that are common in topic.**

Use a variety of ways suggested above. Eliminate repetitious words and group the sentences that have a common topic.

In two weeks it would be Halloween. The boys and girls were preparing for Halloween. The boys and girls were making costumes. They were making costumes out of old clothes. They were having a Halloween party. The Halloween party was at the school. The Halloween party was in the gymnasium. The students in the sixth grade were doing the decorating. The students were hanging cut-outs of ghosts and witches. The students were excited. The students were looking forward to an afternoon off from regular school. There were going to be prizes. The prizes were for the best costumes. Games would be organized. There would be prizes for game winners.

_____

_____

_____

_____

_____

_____

_____

_____

_____

ISBN: 978-1-897457-06-1

Often we are confused by words that sound similar or by words with similar spellings.

C. Read the definitions of the word pairs below and circle the appropriate words for the sentences.

where	a place	among	for more than two things
wear	put on oneself	between	for only two
berth	a place for sleeping	die	pass away
birth	to be born	dye	change colour
accept	receive something	addition	to be added
except	not including	edition	a published section
beside	next to	canvas	cloth for a tent
besides	as well as	canvass	survey people
cloths	fabrics	council	a group brought together
clothes	what we wear	counsel	legal advice
hanged	a person	few	for numbers
hung	a thing	less	for quantity

1. Where, Wear are you?

2. What is your date of berth, birth ?

3. Who is going beside, besides us?

4. She dyed, died her hair for the school play.

5. He will accept, except the award at the ceremony.

6. The defendant sought legal council, counsel before the trial.

7. We will canvas, canvass the neighbourhood for political support.

8. We had to choose among, between the left and the right door.

9. I found an old addition, edition of my favourite book.

10. They shopped for warm cloths, clothes to wear for winter.

11. There were few, less people in attendance.

12. They hanged, hung the picture on the wall.

ISBN: 978-1-897457-06-1

The construction of the Great Pyramid has been a mystery to man for centuries. How did the builders shape and transport over 2,300,000 stones without iron tools and transportation? How did they move these massive blocks that weighed several tons? Why did they go to so much trouble?

In attempting to answer these questions, it is important to understand how the Egyptians related to the world around them. The Egyptians observed the phenomena of nature. They believed in the balance of all things. Sunrise gave way to sunset and nature revolved in repetitive cycles. They were staunch believers in gods. The gods controlled nature and therefore controlled their lives. Egyptians believed in life after death. Similar to the cycles of nature, they believed that they too followed a cycle: birth, life, death, and afterlife. They believed that at death their bodies were transported to a place they called the Land of the Dead where a person could carry on with the rest of his or her existence. To facilitate this transition, they buried their dead with a variety of household tools and items of importance that would make things easier in the afterlife.

Egyptians believed that pharaohs were direct descendants of the gods and were responsible for the order in their lives. Upon their death, pharaohs would enjoy life forever with the gods. It was believed that the pharaohs would cruise the skies watching over their people. Therefore, the pharaohs were even more important to the people after they died.

In approximately 2500 BCE, the pharaoh, Khufu, ascended to the throne and declared himself to be the manifestation of both the gods, Horus and Ra. A claim like this had never been made before and the Egyptians were overwhelmed. They declared that Khufu was the greatest pharaoh of all time.

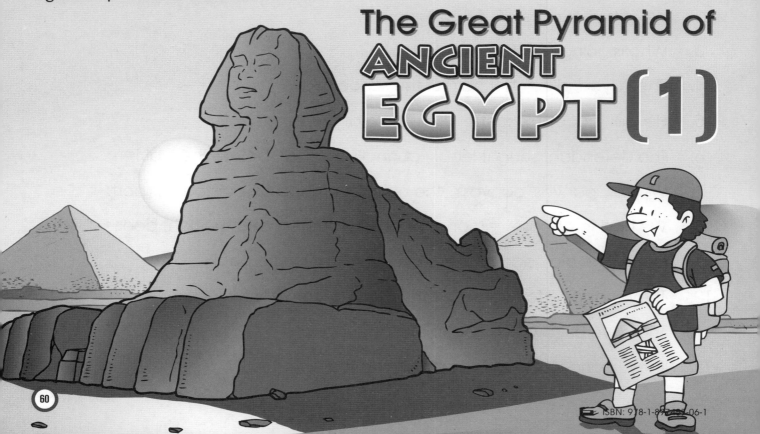

The Great Pyramid of ANCIENT EGYPT (1)

ISBN: 978-1-897457-06-1

Sequence of Events

A. **For each pair of statements, place a check mark before the one that appears first in the passage.**

1. _____ A. Pharaoh Khufu declared himself to be the manifestation of both the gods, Horus and Ra.

   _____ B. Upon their death, pharaohs would enjoy life forever with the gods.

2. _____ A. The construction of the Great Pyramid has been a mystery to man for centuries.

   _____ B. It is important to understand how the Egyptians related to the world around them.

3. _____ A. They were staunch believers in gods.

   _____ B. Therefore, the pharaohs were even more important to the people after they died.

4. _____ A. They declared that Khufu was the greatest pharaoh of all time.

   _____ B. They believed in the balance of all things.

5. _____ A. The Egyptians observed the phenomena of nature.

   _____ B. Egyptians believed that pharaohs were direct descendants of the gods.

6. _____ A. The pharaohs were even more important to the people after they died.

   _____ B. Egyptians believed in life after death.

B. **Could you offer an answer to one of the three questions in the first paragraph of the passage?**

_____

_____

_____

ISBN: 978-1-897457-06-1

The Narrative Paragraph

- A **Narrative Paragraph** gives information, tells a story, or explains something to the readers. It should have a beginning, a middle, and a conclusion.
- The beginning should have a topic sentence that stimulates the readers. It should set up the story by giving introductory facts or information so that the readers can understand the writer's purpose.
- The middle sentences should give all the details.
- The concluding sentence should summarize the purpose of the narrative.

C. Compose a narrative paragraph using one of the following topic sentences.

a. Riding a bicycle is not only good exercise, it is a great means of transportation.

b. In the neighbourhood, there are many ways to earn money doing odd jobs.

c. My summer holidays are always full of wonderful experiences.

d. Christmas season is my favourite time of the year.

_____

_____

_____

_____

_____

_____

_____

_____

_____

_____

_____

ISBN: 978-1-897457-06-1

Word Analogies

- By understanding the relation of a pair of words given, you can figure out other pairs of words that follow the same pattern. In some cases, you have to create a word that is similar in part of speech.

Example: Ride is to riding as drink is to drinking. Similarly, kind is to kindly as ___?___ is to lovely.

The answer above would be "love".

D. Create the parallel word for each of the relationship pairs below.

1. Rely is to reliance as comply is to _____ .

2. Happy is to happiness as sad is to _____ .

3. Able is to ability as reliable is to _____ .

4. Flavour is to flavourless as thought is to _____ .

5. Immediate is to immediately as impolite is to _____ .

6. Gracious is to grace as spacious is to _____ .

7. Courageous is to courage as outrageous is to _____ .

8. Argue is to argument as announce is to _____ .

9. Hopeful is to hope as wasteful is to _____ .

10. Injustice is to justice as _____ is to ability.

11. Disregard is to regard as disrespect is to _____ .

12. Irregular is to regular as _____ is to responsible.

13. Unreliable is to rely as _____ is to deny.

14. Direct is to director as instruct is to _____ .

15. Will not is to won't as cannot is to _____ .

ISBN: 978-1-897457-06-1

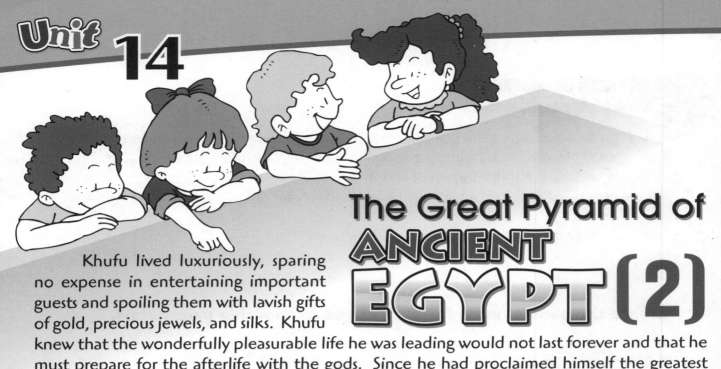

The Great Pyramid of ANCIENT EGYPT (2)

Khufu lived luxuriously, sparing no expense in entertaining important guests and spoiling them with lavish gifts of gold, precious jewels, and silks. Khufu knew that the wonderfully pleasurable life he was leading would not last forever and that he must prepare for the afterlife with the gods. Since he had proclaimed himself the greatest pharaoh of all time, he was compelled to back up his claim by constructing the greatest pyramid of all time.

The location of this great pyramid was important. It had to be in the Western Desert in a location close to the Land of the Dead, yet in a spot unique to him. He chose the Giza Plateau. It was a perfect location. Limestone, the mineral used for building the blocks, was found in abundance at this site. The firmness of the land provided a perfect foundation for the structure and this location happened to rise high above the landscape, creating a monumental presence for his pyramid.

Over 35,000 labourers were drawn from nearby farms to work full time on this project. Many of them became skilled craftsmen after years of work. Various kinds of stones were brought in by boat from quarries hundreds of miles away for the ornamentation of the walls, floor, and chambers. It is believed that the construction of the Great Pyramid took many years.

Khufu died in 2566 BCE after reigning for 23 years. He was mummified, a process lasting 65 days, and lowered into the sarcophagus inside the pyramid. The work of devoted priests and labourers was not yet over as they then bore the responsibility of protecting the tomb and organizing ceremonies to honour the greatest pharaoh of all time.

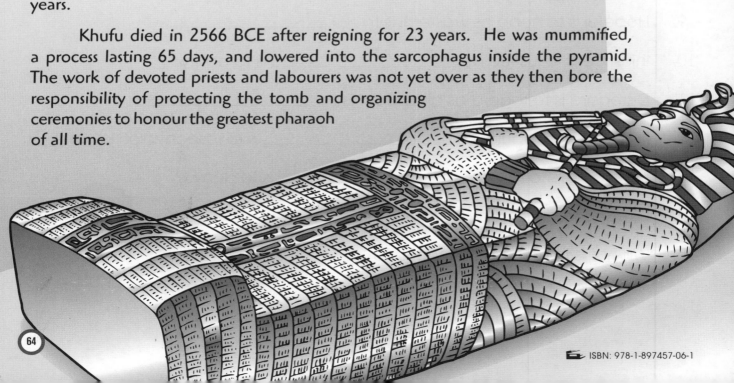

ISBN: 978-1-897457-06-1

Recalling Details

A. **Read each statement and then look at the words listed below. Choose the appropriate word from the list for each space.**

Use these words from the passage to fill in the blanks.

> afterlife   sarcophagus   farms
> firmness   guests   gold   chambers
> landscape   priests   construction
> foundation   jewels   craftsmen   ornamentation
> limestone   labourers   mummified

1. Khufu spared no expense when entertaining _____ .

2. Khufu chose the Giza Plateau for his pyramid because the _____ of the land would support the structure.

3. _____ was the mineral used for building the blocks used in the construction of the pyramid.

4. Khufu needed thousands of _____ to build the pyramid.

5. The builders of the pyramid were taken from nearby _____ .

6. Khufu was _____ to preserve his body.

7. When Khufu died, he was lowered into a _____ .

8. Even though Khufu was young, he knew he had to prepare for the _____ .

9. _____ were responsible for protecting the tomb and organizing ceremonies to honour the pharaoh.

10. The Giza Plateau rose high above the _____ .

11. Boats brought in different kinds of stones for the _____ of the pyramid.

12. It took many years to finish the _____ of the Great Pyramid.

ISBN: 978-1-897457-06-1

Writing a Descriptive Composition

- To write descriptively, use adjectives and adjective phrases to describe nouns, and adverbs and adverb phrases to describe verbs. It is important to have an eye for detail. Colour, size, and shape are important details when describing an object.
- Try appealing to the senses (sight, sound, smell, touch, taste) of the readers.
- Assume you are a camera. Record details as the camera might.

  For example, if you are describing a person, use details from a distance such as size and move in closer for descriptions with finer details such as facial features and gestures. If you are describing a place, move around the location highlighting features in the order that they appear and describe them.

B. **Write a short, detailed, descriptive paragraph on one of the following topics or choose a topic of your own.**

Be sure to use adjectives, adverbs, and action verbs.

the caged animal	first snowfall
the stranger at the door	the substitute teacher
the mountain cave	the messy room

ISBN: 978-1-897457-06-1

Similes

- A **Simile** is a comparison of two things that have some characteristics in common. The word "like" or "as" is used to link the two things that are being compared.
- If someone is a fast runner, you might say that he runs "as fast as a deer". Or you may compare someone's singing talent to that of a bird's by saying, "She sang like a lark".
- Note the use of "like" and "as" to construct the comparison.

C.   Finish each of these statements with a simile.

1.   She was as angry as _____ .

2.   He fought like _____ .

3.   The plane soared like _____ .

4.   The car sped by like _____ .

5.   The child was as quiet as _____ .

6.   The students were as happy as _____ .

Metaphors

- A **Metaphor** is another form of comparison whereby two unlike objects are compared by implying that one thing is the same as the other without using "like" or "as" to set up the comparison.

   Examples: 1. He had pegs for legs.
   2. The reflection was a river of light.

D.   Underline the metaphorical terms.

1.   The troubled boy is a bear to deal with.

2.   The river is the ligament to the inland.

3.   Happiness is the sunshine in life.

4.   The sands of time flow steadily across the desert.

5.   The main road is the artery of the town.

ISBN: 978-1-897457-06-1

With more than 1,000 patented discoveries to his credit, Edison was one of the greatest scientists that profoundly shaped modern society. However, when Edison was young, no one expected him to excel in life.

When he was seven, Edison's family moved from Ohio to Michigan after his father landed a carpentry job at a military post there. Edison entered school in Port Huron but he did not do well at school.

Thomas Edison –
the Greatest Inventor in History

Because of hearing problems, he had difficulty following the lessons and often played truant. However, Edison did not while away his time. Instead, he used the time to read books and set up a laboratory in the basement of his home. But the smell from his laboratory was often so strong that his mother had to stop him from carrying out any more experiments at home.

At the age of twelve, Edison got a job as a train boy on the Grand Trunk Railway. There, he made use of an abandoned freight car as his laboratory. He even learned how to use the telegraph and later became a roving telegrapher in the Midwest, New England, the South, and even Canada. During that time, he successfully developed a device that could transmit messages automatically. By 1869, Edison's inventions in telegraphy were widely adopted, which made him decide to leave the job and become a full-time inventor. Edison's most "well-known" inventions included the electric light bulb, the carbon-button transmitter used in telephone speakers and microphones, and the phonograph. In explaining how he could come up with so many inventions, Edison said, "Genius is one per cent inspiration and ninety-nine per cent perspiration."

Edison died at a ripe old age of 84 on October 18, 1931. At the time of his death, he was still doing experiments in his laboratory in West Orange, New Jersey. He clearly enjoyed his work as an inventor and lived life to its fullest.

ISBN: 978-1-897457-06-1

Recalling Information

A. Place "T" for true and "F" for false in the spaces provided.

1. Edison's father was once a scientist. _____

2. Edison had difficulties in hearing. _____

3. Edison worked for a railway company when he was twelve. _____

4. The electric light bulb was the only thing invented by Edison. _____

5. Edison died in a hotel in New Jersey. _____

B. Answer the following questions.

1. Why did Edison skip classes?

   _____

2. How can we tell that Edison had a passion for learning even when he skipped classes?

   _____

3. Why couldn't Edison continue with his experiments at home?

   _____

4. What skills did he pick up while working as a train boy?

   _____

5. What prompted Edison to leave the job with the Railway?

   _____

Your Opinion

C. Why is it that "Genius is one per cent inspiration and ninety-nine per cent perspiration."?

_____

_____

ISBN: 978-1-897457-06-1

Avoiding Padded Language

- **Padded Language** occurs when a writer becomes wordy when stating a fact or an idea. Sometimes it is the use of clauses or phrases where a single word would suffice.

    Examples: The statement, "It occurs to me that I may be late if I don't hurry.", might simply be written, "I may be late if I don't hurry."
    or
    "What he wants to do is to become a professional athlete." could be written, "He wants to become a professional athlete."

D. Rewrite the following wordy sentences in a more concise way.

1. The reason I want to go to the park is that I want to have fun.

    _____

2. He noticed the key which was in the lock.

    _____

3. The fact is that I really enjoy going to the movies.

    _____

4. In fact, I feel that exercise is beneficial.

    _____

5. In my opinion, I think that the fact is that the school year is too long.

    _____

6. On account of the fact that today is a holiday, most stores are closed.

    _____

7. According to what I remember, he won the championship last year.

    _____

8. The girl who is standing there and who is with a dog is my classmate.

    _____

ISBN: 978-1-897457-06-1

Synonyms

- **Synonyms** *are words that have similar meanings.*
  Examples: *happy – merry; large – big; small – tiny*

E. For each row of words, circle the best synonym for the lead word.

1.	often	seldom	never	frequently	once
2.	difficulty	easy	problem	importance	necessity
3.	profoundly	deeply	easily	quickly	happily
4.	expected	believed	respected	thought	anticipated
5.	start	stop	continue	finish	begin
6.	modern	present	old	moderate	outdated
7.	well-known	notorious	significant	famous	clear
8.	discoveries	uncovers	covers	experiments	inventions

Antonyms

- **Antonyms** *are words that are opposite in meaning.*
  Examples: *long – short; beautiful – ugly; cold – warm*

F. Find an antonym from the passage for each of the following words.

1. manually _____

2. receive _____

3. detested _____

4. stationary _____

5. abandoned _____

6. fail _____

7. continue _____

8. stay _____

ISBN: 978-1-897457-06-1

While Canada and the United States share a common language and many aspects of culture are similar, they differ in the language of measurement. In the early 1970s, Canada started adopting the metric system of measurement widely used throughout Europe. Thus, inches were replaced by centimetres, yards by metres, miles by kilometres, and gallons by litres. By multiplying or dividing by 10, 100, or 1,000, conversions between various lengths and quantities in the metric system are easily calculated.

Measurement, however, was not always so mathematically accurate. The foot, for example, was initially determined to be the length of a person's actual foot. The obvious problem with this measurement was the variety in length of the human foot. Therefore, the foot of a nobleman or leader was used to standardize the length. The inch, which was the width of a thumb, was also somewhat regulated by using the body part of an authority figure.

The Romans, sticklers for accuracy, are credited with establishing the first standard mile. Using the measurement of 5 Roman feet to measure a pace, that is one step, and 1,000 paces to walk a mile, they determined that one mile would equal 5,000 feet as it came to be known. However, this measurement was not acceptable in England because it did not conform to the measurement of 8 furlongs to a mile. A furlong, the common measurement used on farms, was 220 yards, and 8 furlongs (a mile) totalled 5,280 feet, the distance that is used today. England's Henry I proclaimed that the yard should be the distance from his nose to the end of his thumb on his outstretched arm. Before Henry's declaration, the yard was the length of a girdle around the king's waist which would have increased greatly had they used the waistline of Henry VIII.

The British, who were the originators of this non-metric system still used by Americans today, also switched to the metric system to simplify the mathematics of measurement. For the Americans to follow suit would be a costly venture but one that would be embraced by schoolchildren plagued by learning the inconsistent measurement tables of inches, feet, yards, ounces, pounds, and tons.

Accurate Measurement
Was Not Always Accurate

5 feet

3 feet

ISBN 978-1-897457-06-1

Matching Details

A. Match the facts by drawing lines from Column A to Column B.

Column A		Column B
1. centimetres	•	• body part of an official
2. standardized measurement	•	• width of a thumb
3. established first mile	•	• 8 furlongs
4. his nose to his thumb	•	• 5,000 feet
5. mile	•	• 220 yards
6. furlong	•	• Canada adopted the metric system
7. Roman mile	•	• Romans
8. inch	•	• British
9. 1970s	•	• replaced the inches for measurement
10. began non-metric system	•	• Henry I

B. Answer the questions.

1. Which description in the passage suggests that Henry VIII was very fat?

_____

_____

2. Why is the metric system considered an easier measurement system to use? Give an example of using the measurement.

_____

_____

3. Why would it be costly for the Americans to switch to the metric system?

_____

_____

ISBN: 978-1-897457-06-1

The Overloaded Sentence

- **Sentences** become **overloaded** when we fail to create the necessary sentence breaks. Remember, a sentence contains a complete thought and although we can make our sentences more interesting by adding phrases and clauses, we must be careful not to create overly long sentences.

- The paragraph below contains overloaded sentences. Read the paragraph and the revised one. Note the changes.

2 sentences

The class party was scheduled for the last Friday in December before the Christmas break and all the students were excited because we were drawing names for presents and no one knew who had drawn his or her name. Finally, the day of the party arrived and the excitement was building until we were able to go and get our gift from under the tree and try to guess who had bought the gift for us.

become

5 sentences

The class party was scheduled for the last Friday in December before the Christmas break. All the students were excited because we were drawing names for presents and no one knew who had drawn his or her name. Finally, the day of the party arrived. The excitement was building until we were able to go and get our gift from under the tree. We tried to guess who had bought the gift for us.

C. Revise the following paragraph, putting in the necessary sentence breaks.

We were packed and ready to go to the airport early in the morning because our flight was scheduled for 7:00 a.m. and we were told to be there two hours ahead of time. Luckily there was no traffic on the roads and we arrived on time to check in at the airline desk where they took our baggage and gave us our boarding passes. Soon we were on the plane and on our way to our holiday destination that promised to be a wonderful vacation spot that would always be remembered.

_____

_____

_____

_____

_____

_____

_____

ISBN: 978-1-897457-06-1

Descriptive Language

- Your writing may be enhanced by using vivid language to replace ordinary, less colourful words.

  Example: The word "big" might be replaced by "huge", "enormous", or "gigantic", or a word such as "leave" might be replaced by "depart" or "abandon".

D. **Replace the underlined word with a more descriptive word from the list of words provided.**

positioned	scampered	ecstatic	visited	cavernous

1. He was <u>happy</u> to be here.   _____

2. The children <u>ran</u> out to play.   _____

3. He <u>came to</u> the cottage last summer.   _____

4. They <u>put</u> the picture on the wall.   _____

5. The <u>large</u> canyon could not be crossed.   _____

E. **Fill in the blanks with descriptive words from the list below.**

refresh	swooped	enjoy	cool	peaceful
towering	green	leaned	gentle	flowed

The 1._____ river 2._____ calmly

through the 3._____ valley. On either side of the river

grew 4._____ oaks whose branches swayed and

5._____ towards the riverbank.

Birds 6._____ down to dip their beaks and

7._____ a drink of 8._____ water. Forest

animals also cautiously approached the bank to 9._____

themselves. Life in the valley was 10._____ .

The names "Bermuda Triangle" or "Devil's Triangle" as it is referred to by some are unofficial titles for the triangular area of the Atlantic between Miami, Florida, Bermuda, and San Juan, Puerto Rico. The area covers over a million square kilometres of ocean and is famous for the unexplained disappearances of numerous ships, small crafts, and airplanes. Notable is the mysterious vanishing of the entire US Navy flight squadron, Flight 19.

There are two schools of thought on these disappearances. One is the popular belief that supernatural forces were at play. Some theorize that the devil was doing his handiwork. Some theorize that aliens sucked up both the crafts and the occupants through a vacuum-like funnel hurling them into space and whisking them away to another planet. One thing is certain. There were very strange forces at work during these disappearances, and logical theories and explanations have fallen short of satisfying the skeptics.

A more rational way of thinking is to consider the many natural explanations. This part of the Atlantic is subject to sudden storms. The Gulf Stream, which flows through this part of the Atlantic, can swiftly erase evidence of disasters at sea. The ocean floor there is a mixture of shoals and deep trenches, creating unpredictable marine conditions. In addition to environmental factors is the concept of human error. People travel in this area in crafts that are too small to withstand the conditions, and without the experience to respond adequately when conditions change.

The US Coast Guard prefer to dispel any notion of supernatural or extraterrestrial forces at play. They prefer to adopt the rational viewpoint that human error, natural forces, and coincidence are factors responsible for these unsolved disasters. However, the mysterious disappearance of Flight 19 and the haunting pleas of the disoriented flight leader of that mission, Lt. Taylor, strongly suggest that there was more than nature at work on that fateful December day in 1945.

The Mystery of Flight 19 (1)

ISBN: 978-1-897457-06-1

Recalling Facts

A. Place "T" for true and "F" for false beside each statement.

1. The other name for the Bermuda Triangle is Danger Zone. _____

2. The Bermuda Triangle is located between Miami, Bermuda, and Puerto Rico. _____

3. The Bermuda Triangle is the official name of this location. _____

4. One of the strangest disappearances was that of Flight 19. _____

5. Some people believe aliens captured the missing vessels. _____

6. There are no possible natural causes of the disappearances. _____

7. Human error is considered a possible explanation for the disappearances. _____

8. The US Coast Guard believe that supernatural forces were at play in the Triangle. _____

9. Lt. Taylor was not concerned by the strange events in the Triangle. _____

Using Information to Form Opinion

B. Briefly summarize the "two schools of thought" which attempt to explain the strange occurrences in the Bermuda Triangle.

1. Natural Causes:

_____

_____

2. Supernatural Causes:

_____

_____

3. Which do you believe is true? Explain.

_____

_____

ISBN: 978-1-897457-06-1

Faulty Sentences

- A **Comma Splice** is a common error in forming sentences. This occurs when two thoughts are fused together without one of them being converted into a subordinate clause.

    Example: The boy ran up the hill, he was really tired.
    In this example, the second thought is tacked onto the first and separated by a comma. There are a few ways to fix this problem:

- First, use a conjunction.
  The boy ran up the hill and he was really tired.

- Second, change one thought to a subordinate clause.
  Because the boy ran up the hill, he was really tired. or After the boy ran up the hill, he was really tired.

- Third, use a semicolon. This allows you to connect two principal clauses that have a common idea giving equal importance to each.
  The boy ran up the hill; hence he was really tired. Notice the addition of the sentence connector.

C. Repair the following comma splices.

1. The game was over, we left the arena together.

    _____

2. They were shopping for a gift, they could not find one they liked.

    _____

3. The recess bell sounded, the schoolchildren played in the yard.

    _____

4. The dog barked at the mailman, he delivered the letters.

    _____

5. The runners took their positions, the race was on.

    _____

6. The teacher spoke loudly, we still couldn't hear him.

    _____

ISBN: 978-1-897457-06-1

Writing Poetry

- **Haiku Poetry**

  Haiku is a Japanese form of poetry writing that uses very precise and descriptive language. A Haiku poem consists of three lines of five, seven, and five syllables respectively.

  Example:

  > Beach Holiday
  > Ocean waves bright blue
  > Sunshine, sailboats, and sea breeze
  > Summer at the beach

- The first line in the sample consists of 5 syllables, the second – 7 syllables, and the third – 5 syllables. Also, note the use of words that begin with the same letters. These are called alliterations and they are an effective, descriptive technique.

- When composing a Haiku poem, you should leave out unnecessary words since you are restricted by the number of syllables for each line. Use descriptive words that create picturesque images.

D. Compose a Haiku poem for each of the titles below. Or, create your own title.

Seasons

Beauty

Friendship

Stormy Night

ISBN: 978-1-897457-06-1

The Mystery of Flight 19 (2)

On December 5, 1945, five Avenger torpedo bombers carrying 14 men left the Naval Air Station at Fort Lauderdale, Florida on a routine training flight. None of the men returned home and none of the 5 planes were found. Of the 14 men on this fateful flight, 13 were trainees. Their mission was to practise bombing at a location 60 miles east. Once the practice mission was completed, they were to continue in an easterly direction for approximately another 70 miles, turn north for 70 miles, and then turn southwest and head for home. In effect, they were unwittingly travelling a route that resembled the formation of the Bermuda Triangle.

Suddenly, a radio broadcast was intercepted from one of the crew of Flight 19 stating that he didn't know where he was. Lt. Cox, the pilot who originally overheard the distress message, tried to make contact with the crew. After much effort, he finally connected with Lt. Taylor who informed him that his compasses were not working. Lt. Taylor stated that he thought he was in the Florida Keys, a string of islands extending from the southern tip of Florida. Cox then told Taylor to fly north. Taylor was not in the Keys but likely in the Bahamas. Following Cox's advice would have sent him out into the ocean. When instructed by the tower to head west, Taylor stated that he couldn't find west and that the ocean looked very strange. This was curious because Taylor could have simply used the sun to navigate his way.

The Navy sent out the Martin Mariner flight-boat with a crew of 13 to search for Flight 19. It too disappeared. Now there were 27 men missing. With the sun setting and radio transmission failing, the Fort Lauderdale Naval Base became increasingly concerned for the safety of the men. Fuel in the aircraft was running low and to complicate matters further, a storm was moving into the area. At 7:00 p.m., Taylor made his final radio transmission. Search and rescue crews fought through stormy weather for most of the night in a desperate attempt to find any evidence of the fate of Flight 19 and the Martin Mariner. No trace of either was ever found.

ISBN: 978-1-897457-06-1

Listing Facts

A. **List three important facts for each of the following paragraphs in the reading passage.**

1. **Paragraph One**

   _____

   _____

   _____

2. **Paragraph Two**

   _____

   _____

   _____

3. **Paragraph Three**

   _____

   _____

   _____

Using Facts to Build an Argument

B. **Suppose your task was to prove that supernatural forces were the real cause of the disappearances in the Bermuda Triangle. List the most important facts that you would use to build your case.**

1. _____

2. _____

3. _____

4. _____

5. _____

6. _____

ISBN: 978-1-897457-06-1

Frequently Misspelled Words

- Some words are frequently misspelled. These words are not unusual or particularly difficult. Some of these words sound or look proper even when spelled incorrectly.

C. **In each pair of words, one word is misspelled. Circle the word that is spelled correctly.**

1.	massacre	massacer	2.	monitor	moniter
3.	lives	lifes	4.	fourty	forty
5.	heros	heroes	6.	barely	bearly
7.	goverment	government	8.	existense	existence
9.	seize	sieze	10.	atheletic	athletic
11.	beautiful	beautifull	12.	wether	whether
13.	ninth	nineth	14.	neccessary	necessary
15.	independant	independent	16.	kangaroo	kangeroo
17.	comparison	comparision	18.	truely	truly
19.	embarrassed	emberassed	20.	luckly	luckily
21.	occasion	ocassion	22.	develope	develop
23.	sking	skiing	24.	accommodate	accomodate
25.	tution	tuition	26.	vedio	video

ISBN: 978-1-897457-06-1

The Friendly Letter

Your letter may include: family news, an update on how you are doing at school, future plans, sports or clubs that you are participating in, asking how your friend is doing, etc. Note also the proper way to address your envelope.

D. **Write a letter to a friend, classmate, or relative using the format below.**

Format

Your Address

_____

_____

_____

Salutation *(Dear Uncle Bill or Hi old friend)*

_____

The Body of the Letter

_____

_____

_____

_____

Yours truly,

Signature _____

The Envelope

Your address goes here.

Place stamp here.

The address of the person to whom you are writing goes here.

ISBN: 978-1-897457-06-1

Recalling Facts

A. **For each statement, fill in the blank with the appropriate answer from the choices.**

1. Guinness World Records was originated by a _____ company.

    clothing   beer   wine   publishing

2. There are an estimated _____ words in the Oxford Dictionary.

    750,000   500,000   1,000,000   150,000

3. The first actual computer was built by the US Army in _____ .

    1973   1982   1946   1962

4. The Egyptians believed that the _____ controlled nature.

    gods   stars   pharaohs   kings

5. The _____ are credited historically with establishing the first mile.

    British   French   Romans   Egyptians

6. Thomas Edison worked for a _____ company at the age of twelve.

    shipping   railway   clothing   metal

7. The pharaoh, Khufu, for whom the Great Pyramid was built, died at the age of _____ .

    35   23   51   14

8. There were _____ men on Flight 19 lost in the Bermuda Triangle.

    26   14   9   18

9. In the world today, there are an estimated _____ languages.

    200   2,000   2,700   450

10. The first electronic computer produced by the United States was called the

    _____ .

    R2D2   ENIAC   LAPTOP   LOTUS

ISBN: 978-1-897457-06-1

B. Place "T" for true and "F" for false in the spaces provided.

1. The Guinness Book was originally a promotional idea. _____

2. It is believed that over a billion people use the English language today. _____

3. The roots of the computer go back to an American inventor. _____

4. Originally computers were used only for games. _____

5. The Egyptians believed that the pharaohs were descendents of the gods. _____

6. The pharaoh, Khufu, declared himself a descendent of the gods, Horus and Ra. _____

7. The pharaoh, Khufu, refused to spend money. _____

8. Very few labourers were involved in building the pyramids. _____

9. The first mile was a measurement of only 5,000 feet. _____

10. The non-metric system was invented by the British. _____

11. The Devil's Triangle is another name for the Bermuda Triangle. _____

12. Thomas Edison skipped classes to work as a train boy. _____

13. Thomas Edison did experiments in his basement. _____

14. One of the Avenger torpedo bombers crashed into the sea. _____

15. The Avenger crew never made contact by radio to signal they were in trouble. _____

16. Crew commander Taylor had no trouble with directions. _____

17. The disappearance of Flight 19 was determined to be due to human error. _____

ISBN: 978-1-897457-06-1

Combining Sentences

C. **Combine each group of simple sentences into one sentence. It can be a compound, complex, or compound-complex sentence.**

1. Sharon's family moved from Montreal to Toronto. She was six then.

   _____

2. Charles likes his new bike very much. He rides it to the park every day.

   _____

3. It has been snowing in the past few days. The roads are slippery. People have to drive slowly.

   _____

   _____

Punctuating Sentences

D. **Place the appropriate punctuation marks in the sentences below.**

1. When I go sailing I get seasick
2. How many eggs do you need for the cake
3. After you check in your luggage you get your boarding pass
4. Slow down You are moving too fast

Synonyms and Antonyms

E. **Write the synonyms and antonyms for the words below.**

	Synonym	Antonym
1. famous	_____	_____
2. expected	_____	_____
3. modern	_____	_____
4. difficult	_____	_____
5. costly	_____	_____

ISBN: 978-1-897457-06-1

Avoiding Padded Language

F. **Remove unnecessary words in each of the sentences below. You may have to alter the order of the words.**

1. What I want to do is to go shopping.

   _____

2. In my opinion, I think that if you study hard you will be a success.

   _____

3. As a result of the fact that the team did not have enough players they defaulted the game and ended up losing.

   _____

4. The fact is that the dog follows me wherever I go.

   _____

Combining Sentences

G. **Combine the following groups of sentences into one sentence. Use a semicolon, a conjunction, or a subordinate clause.**

1. It was raining. I was walking home. I got all wet.

   _____

2. The dog barked. The man knocked on the door. The man was frightened.

   _____

3. The traffic was building. Rush hour was upon us. It was 5:00 p.m.

   _____

4. She was unhappy. She had lost her bracelet. Her mother gave her the bracelet.

   _____

ISBN: 978-1-897457-06-1

Developing Vocabulary

Words that sound the same and have similar spellings are often confused.

H. In each sentence, write the correct word from the choices in the space provided.

1. Everyone did well in the show accept, except _____ Kevin.

2. The birth, berth _____ of the child was a reason for celebration.

3. The children all needed new cloths, clothes _____ .

4. Do you know where, wear _____ the new shopping mall is?

5. In edition, addition _____ to winning the scoring title, she was chosen as the Most Valuable Player on the team.

6. Besides, Beside _____ the dresser, you will find the magazines.

7. Your canvas, canvass _____ bag looks really nice.

Building New Words

I. Create a new word from each of the base or root words provided.

| **Example:** | "Happy" becomes "happily" as an adverb and "happiness" as a noun. |

	Root Word	Change to – Part of Speech	Becomes – New Word
1.	excite	noun	
2.	beauty	adjective	
3.	create	adjective	
4.	sly	adverb	
5.	surprise	adverb	
6.	loud	noun	
7.	erupt	noun	

ISBN: 978-1-897457-06-1

Creating New Forms of Words

J. **Change each of the following words to another form based on the hint given.**

1.	popular	– a large number of people added together	=
2.	action	– a man who performs on a stage	=
3.	excite	– gets excited easily	=
4.	kind	– spread this around and you will be liked	=
5.	confide	– if you believe, then you have this	=
6.	react	– this comes when it happens	=
7.	separate	– the split is called this	=
8.	utilize	– usefulness	=
9.	repeat	– if it keeps happening, it is this	=
10.	peace	– someone who makes peace	=
11.	virtue	– showing higher moral principles	=
12.	will	– if you won't do it, you are this	=
13.	delicate	– found in the bakery	=
14.	deny	– you can't deny this	=
15.	respect	– never show this to anyone	=

ISBN: 978-1-897457-06-1

ISBN: 978-1-897457-06-1

ISBN: 978-1-897457-06-1

Parts of Speech

Grammar explains the role each type of word plays in a phrase or a sentence. We refer to the various word types as "**parts of speech**". There are eight parts of speech in English.

Noun: to name a person, a place, an object, an idea, or a feeling
Pronoun: to stand in for a noun
Verb: to describe an action or a state of being
Adjective: to describe a noun or a pronoun

A. Underline the nouns in the following sentences.

1. The restaurant serves Italian food.

2. Beauty is in the eye of the beholder.

3. The teacher wrote a poem about friendship.

4. Where can you find a better place than this?

5. The house was destroyed in the storm.

6. In the end, she was left with a sense of emptiness.

B. Complete the paragraph about Ted with pronouns.

"1._____ on earth is the gossip about?" wondered Ted. At first,

2._____ thought that 3._____ was the one his neighbours were

talking about but soon realized that 4._____ weren't talking about

5._____ . 6._____ was just being too sensitive and had almost

made a fool of 7._____ . Luckily, Ted's sister did not know about

8._____ or 9._____ would tell 10._____ parents.

ISBN: 978-1-897457-06-1

C. Circle the verbs in the following paragraph.

Did you know a monster might be living in a lake in Scotland? Numerous people have reported sightings of the Loch Ness Monster over the years but there has never been any scientific evidence that it really exists. Photographs and videos of the creature have surfaced but many have been revealed to be hoaxes or turned out to be various objects mistaken as the monster. The Loch Ness Monster has not caused any harm to humans and many people still hope to see it.

D. Complete the following paragraph about hockey with suitable adjectives.

British	difficult	amateur	frozen	national	silver	frigid

It is 1._____ to argue that hockey is not the 2._____ passion of Canadians. Canada, with its 3._____ winter weather, is suitable for playing hockey. As early as 1870, 4._____ soldiers stationed in Halifax started playing hockey games on 5._____ ponds around the city. In 1892, Lord Stanley, the Governor General of Canada, donated a 6._____ bowl to be awarded to the best 7._____ team. That was the origin of the Stanley Cup.

The other four parts of speech are: adverb, preposition, conjunction, and interjection.

Adverb: to modify the meaning of a verb, an adjective, or another adverb
Preposition: to express the relationship between words
Conjunction: to join words or phrases together
Interjection: to express emotion or excitement

E. Add adverbs to the following sentences. Use "∧" to show where they should be put.

> rather   knowingly   exceptionally   cautiously   almost

1. That performance was good.

2. It has been a year since we last saw him.

3. He was not good at that and did it oddly.

4. The slope was steep and they had to go down.

5. He nodded and started figuring out how to settle the matter.

F. Add prepositions to the following paragraph about J.K. Rowling.

Joanne Kathleen Rowling, author 1._____ the immensely popular Harry Potter series, went 2._____ ordinary existence 3._____ stardom virtually overnight. The fame bestowed 4._____ her was 5._____ her wildest dreams. As a single parent 6._____ little money, Joanne often headed 7._____ a café 8._____ write 9._____ the wizard and "Muggle" worlds.

G. Complete the following sentences with suitable conjunctions.

1. Both Mom and Dad like the bungalow _____ it is rather old _____ plain.

2. They were all surprised _____ they never expected me to win.

3. You can't go _____ you finish the work before noon.

4. He declined our offer _____ promised to help us out on weekends.

5. They became impatient _____ time was running out.

6. We will have a game of hockey _____ we have time.

7. You can have this one _____ that one _____ not both.

H. Add a suitable interjection to each of the following sentences.

| Hurray | Yuck | Wow | Oops | Oh no | Great | Hey | Look out |

1. _____ ! I didn't realize it was the teacher; I thought it was Sam.

2. _____ ! That's the longest home run I've seen.

3. _____ ! Let's start right away.

4. _____ ! That's not the way to do it.

5. _____ ! Our team won again.

6. _____ ! A truck is coming right at you.

7. _____ ! It tastes awful.

8. _____ ! I dropped the vase.

ISBN: 978-1-897457-06-1

Tense and Voice

Basically, the **verb** is for expressing action or a state of being. However, the functions of the verb go beyond that. It tells us the tense, voice, and mood of the sentence too.

The **tense** of a sentence tells us when an action occurred or will occur.

Examples: Dan <u>jumped</u> into the ditch and <u>hurt</u> his leg.
        He <u>will not do</u> that again.

The **voice** of a sentence shows the relationship between the verb and the subject. The **active voice** shows that the subject is doing the action whereas the **passive voice** shows that the subject is receiving the action.

Examples: The puppy bit me.   (active voice)
        I was bitten by the puppy.   (passive voice)

A.   Change the voice in the following sentences. Keep to the same tenses.

1.   The children picked the ripe apples.

    _____

2.   The police officer warned the careless driver.

    _____

3.   The books were borrowed by Sue for the project.

    _____

4.   We will decorate the classroom for the party.

    _____

    _____

5.   Darrel left the puppy in the backyard.

    _____

    _____

ISBN: 978-1-897457-06-1

Mood

The **mood** of a sentence tells us in what manner the verb is communicating the action.

The **indicative mood** is used to make a basic statement or ask a question.
Example: We'll have pizza for lunch at school tomorrow.

The **imperative mood** is used to make a command or request.
Example: Please pass the salt to me.

The **subjunctive mood** is used to set up a hypothetical case or express a wish.
Example: I wish I could fly.

B. Indicate the mood in each of the following sentences. Write "IN" for indicative mood, "IM" for imperative mood, and "SUB" for subjunctive mood.

1. Can you tell your sister not to disturb us when we are working?   _____

2. It is a group project that accounts for 30% of the final score.   _____

3. Go to the library to borrow some books for the project.   _____

4. Matt hasn't finished compiling the data yet.   _____

5. How I wish we had more time for the project.   _____

C. Write a sentence of your own using each type of mood.

1. Indicative Mood

    _____

2. Imperative Mood

    _____

3. Subjunctive Mood

    _____

More on the Subjunctive Mood

We use the **subjunctive mood** to indicate a wish, a hypothetical case, a suggestion, or a demand.

Examples: If I <u>were</u> the coach, I would not let him close the game.
(Unfortunately, I am not the coach so there was no way I could stop him being the closer.)
If he <u>were</u> with us, it would be a lot more fun.
(But he wasn't with us.)
The teacher suggested that he <u>think</u> about it before getting back to her.
Her mother demanded that she <u>stay</u> home.

Note the use of "were" in indicating wishes and hypothetical cases, and the base verb in making suggestions or demands.

D. Change the verbs where necessary to reflect the subjunctive mood.

1. How I wish Jane is here with us.

   _____

   _____

2. We looked at him as though he is a monster.

   _____

3. If I am you, I will accept the offer right away.

   _____

4. Her parents demanded that she paid for the repair.

   _____

5. If Sam is the organizer, the show would be much better.

   _____

   _____

ISBN: 978-1-897457-06-1

E. Read the following groups of sentences. Write a sentence in the subjunctive mood to show the main idea of each group.

Example: We all wanted Ted to play in the game. Unfortunately, Ted was sick and could not play. With Ted, we would have a better chance of winning.

<u>If Ted were to play in the game, we would have a better chance of winning.</u>

1. Valerie was busy with her project. It was past midnight but there was still a lot to do. Valerie's mother told her to leave it until the next day.

   _____

2. Mr. Sherwood wants to stay fit. The doctor tells him to get up earlier and exercise for half an hour before going to work.

   _____

3. Jeremy was rude to Patricia. The teacher knew about it. She wanted Jeremy to apologize to Patricia.

   _____

4. At the party, Janet socialized with everyone that came her way. She appeared more like the hostess than a guest.

   _____

5. Julie did rather poorly in comprehension. Mrs. Brown told her that if she wanted to have any improvement, she needed to read more.

   _____

6. Debbie went to an amusement park with her parents. She wanted to ride on the roller-coaster, but her father told her that she was not tall enough. She was very disappointed.

   _____

unit 3 Verbals

> ## Verbals
>
> **Verbals** are formed from verbs but function as nouns, adjectives, or adverbs. There are three types of verbals: gerunds, participles, and infinitives.
>
> **Gerunds** end in "ing" and function as nouns.
> *Example*:   <u>Fishing</u> is my father's favourite pastime in the summer.
>
> **Participles** are verbals that are used as adjectives.
> *Examples*:   The pirates found the <u>hidden</u> treasure. (past participle)
>   Shirley put on her <u>dancing</u> shoes and was all ready for the performance.
>   (present participle)
>
> **Infinitives** can be nouns, adjectives, or adverbs. They are the "to" form of verbs.
> *Example*:   <u>To win</u> the game was the only thing that mattered to them.

A. Underline the verbals in the following sentences and state whether they are gerunds (G), participles (P), or infinitives (I).

1. Keith wants to become a successful scientist. ____

2. We always enjoy swimming in the pool. ____

3. The cooling fan is very noisy. ____

4. Judy just made herself a laughing stock. ____

5. The snow made it difficult for us to see. ____

6. Some say that cooking is an art. ____

7. My mom and dad enjoy jogging in the morning. ____

8. The children greeted the crossing guard warmly. ____

9. To settle the debt is what concerns him most. ____

10. They were about to leave when they heard someone knocking at the door. ____

11. Grandpa doesn't like driving at night. ____

                ISBN: 978-1-897457-06-1

B. Use each of the following verbs as a gerund, a participle, and an infinitive.

1.

ski

G: _____

P: _____

I: _____

2.

skip

G: _____

P: _____

I: _____

3.

float

G: _____

P: _____

I: _____

4.

shop

G: _____

P: _____

I: _____

5.

run

G: _____

P: _____

I: _____

ISBN: 978-1-897457-06-1

Verbal Phrases

A **verbal phrase** contains a gerund, a participle, or an infinitive. It functions as a noun, an adjective, or an adverb.

Examples: The winning pitcher waved at the cheering crowd.
Fishing in the bitter cold is a test of will.
He doesn't want to leave her behind.

C. Underline the verbal phrase(s) in each of the following sentences.

1. Dad took us on a skiing trip.

2. Skiing downhill was much more difficult than I had thought.

3. It was difficult to keep my balance on the slippery slope.

4. The little children enjoyed tobogganing more than skiing.

5. Exhausted after the practice, we suggested taking a rest.

6. There were many other beginning skiers like me.

7. Drinking a cup of hot chocolate was the best reward after the skiing lesson.

8. My sister looked helpless sitting in the snow.

9. She discovered something buried deep in the snow.

10. It was a torn mitten!

ISBN: 978-1-897457-06-1

D. **State whether each infinitive phrase below is used as a noun (N), an adjective (ADJ), or an adverb (ADV).**

1. <u>To complete the work in one day</u> is nearly impossible. ———

2. She wanted <u>to learn knitting</u>. ———

3. The children went home <u>to eat their supper</u>. ———

4. Her mother made her a hat <u>to wear at the party</u>. ———

5. The team wasn't ready <u>to quit the game</u>. ———

E. **Write sentences using the following gerund, participle, or infinitive phrases.**

1. skating on the frozen pond

   _____

2. stuck in the traffic jam

   _____

3. writing a journal entry

   _____

4. to be a good basketball player

   _____

5. enjoying a lazy afternoon

   _____

6. to write an e-mail

   _____

7. tired of waiting

   _____

8. camping in the provincial park

   _____

ISBN: 978-1-897457-06-1

Phrases

A **phrase** is a group of words that has no subject or predicate. There are three types of phrases: noun phrases, adjective phrases, and adverb phrases.

A **noun phrase** is made up of a noun and all its modifiers.

Examples: They were locked up in <u>a small and stuffy room</u>.
<u>All grade one students</u> were told to stay in the hall.

A. Underline the noun phrase(s) in each of the following sentences.

1. The red, sleek sports car sped past me like an arrow.

2. The losing team put up a good fight to the end.

3. We were all exhausted after the long, uphill climb.

4. She always enjoys a cool, refreshing drink by the pool.

5. We never expected such a warm and fun reception.

6. There are altogether seven honour students in our class.

7. Mother baked a delicious cheesecake for us.

8. I was shocked to see the fluffy, creepy thing.

9. The long, bumpy ride lasted almost an hour.

10. No one knew what that thick, oily substance was.

11. All of us thought it was an extremely boring movie.

12. He is the most skilful player we have ever met.

Adjective and Adverb Phrases

An **adjective phrase** describes a noun.

Example: This <u>steaming hot chicken pot</u> pie is my favourite dish.

An **adverb phrase** describes a verb.

Example: I know <u>quite surely</u> what she wants.

Many adjective phrases and adverb phrases are introduced by prepositions. A preposition is a linking word between a noun or a pronoun and other words in a sentence.

Examples: The tourists <u>on the boat</u> are amazed by the spectacular sight.
                The soldiers marched <u>across the field</u>.

B. Underline the adjective phrases and place parentheses around the adverb phrases in the following sentences. Circle the prepositions introducing the phrases if there are any.

1. The coach of the opposing team did not think it was fair.

2. That afternoon, all the workers assembled in the compound.

3. The fugitive crawled through the tunnel and escaped.

4. The members of the team were each given a name tag.

5. No one from his group wanted to do the presentation.

6. Fred played video games from morning to night.

7. All the guests waited in the hallway.

8. His dog managed to jump across the ditch.

9. The food in the cooler had gone bad.

10. He climbed up the tall tree to save the cat.

11. The jellybeans were scattered all over the place.

12. The guards of the palace ordered them to leave.

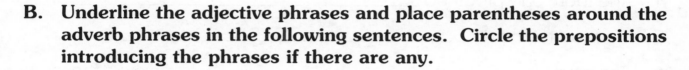

C. Fill in the blanks with the appropriate adjective phrases or adverb phrases.

in the pool   on the bench   soft and beautiful   on weekends
from the daycare centre   very quickly

1. The children were swimming _____ .

2. The man sitting _____ is our coach.

3. She bought the _____ skirt.

4. The team only practised _____ .

5. He read the book _____ .

6. The children _____ enjoyed the show.

D. Rewrite each of the following sentences by adding an adjective phrase.

1. I like the puppy.

   _____

2. The woman is my aunt.

   _____

3. The backpack belongs to my sister.

   _____

4. The clowns bumped into one another.

   _____

5. The man did not allow us in.

   _____

6. Who is the man?

   _____

ISBN: 978-1-897457-06-1

E.   Rewrite each of the following sentences by adding an adverb phrase.

1.   The hurricane blew.

_____

2.   All of us waited.

_____

3.   The grade six boys were practising.

_____

4.   One of the children stopped.

_____

5.   The sprinters dashed.

_____

6.   They walked.

_____

7.   The choir sang.

_____

F.   For each type of phrase below, write a sentence that contains a phrase with a preposition and one without.

Adjective Phrase

1.   _____

2.   _____

Adverb Phrase

1.   _____

2.   _____

ISBN: 978-1-897457-06-1

> ## Direct and Indirect Speech
>
> **Direct speech** repeats the exact words spoken; these words are put in between quotation marks.
>
> *Example*:   Mrs. Martin said to Paul, "You can take one."
>
> **Indirect speech** reports what someone else said; no quotation marks are needed.
>
> *Example*:   Mrs. Martin told Paul that he could take one.
>
> Changing direct speech to indirect speech involves tense changes; the tense in indirect speech is one tense back in time from that in direct speech.
>
> We don't need to change the tense if the reporting verb is in the present tense, or if the statement is about something that is still true.

A.   Change the following sentences to indirect speech.

1.   Ted explained, "The moon revolves around the Earth."

_____

_____

2.   "I like the cotton dress more," said Mabel.

_____

3.   "I will attend the ceremony," said Fred's father.

_____

4.   Karen said, "I'm never good at singing."

_____

5.   Ivan says, "I always enjoy window-shopping with them."

_____

6.   "We've tried many ways," Evelyn said to Mrs. Wayne.

_____

ISBN: 978-1-897457-06-1

Direct Speech to Indirect Speech: Other Changes

Time Reference

In indirect speech, we need to change time reference.

Example: Dan said, "They will hold a garage sale <u>next week</u>."

Dan said that they would hold a garage sale <u>the following week</u>.

Personal Pronouns

We need to change personal pronouns to the third person singular or plural, except when the speaker reports his own words.

Example: Ms. Weir said to him, "<u>I</u> like what <u>you</u> did."

Ms. Weir told him that <u>she</u> liked what <u>he</u> had done.

B.   Change the following sentences to indirect speech using the time references provided.

> the day before   two days later   the following week
> the week before   that day   a week before

1.   "I didn't play in the game yesterday," said Alex to his father.

   _____

2.   "It happened a week ago," said Ron.

   _____

3.   "Grandma will come the day after tomorrow," said Molly.

   _____

4.   The waiter said, "We serve fresh seafood today."

   _____

5.   The teacher said, "Next week, there will be two new students in our class."

   _____

6.   "They went to Hamilton last week," said Bill.

   _____

Direct Questions and Indirect Questions

Note the following when changing direct questions to indirect questions:

- The tense in indirect questions is one tense back in time from that in direct questions.
- There is no need to use "Do/Does/Did".
- Change "Yes/No" questions by using "ask if/whether...".

  Example: One of the players asked, "Will I be sidelined?"
  One of the players <u>asked if</u> he would be sidelined.

C. Change the following questions to indirect speech.

1. "Which is the one you want?" Mrs. Watson asked Ben.

   _____

   _____

2. They asked, "When can we start?"

   _____

3. "Did you come that way?" the police officer asked.

   _____

4. She asked him, "Are you going with me tomorrow?"

   _____

5. "Have you seen my cat?" Mrs. Healey asked her neighbour.

   _____

6. "What is your name?" Angela asked the boy.

   _____

7. The lady asked the cashier, "How much do I owe?"

   _____

ISBN: 978-1-897457-06-1

D. Change the following indirect statements to direct questions.

1. The woman asked if they could take her to their school.

   _____

2. Carol asked Bill if he had got an MP3 player.

   _____

3. The delivery man asked if there was anyone in the house.

   _____

4. I asked him if he had seen my Science book.

   _____

5. The librarian asked if I had borrowed the storybook.

   _____

6. The waitress asked us if we were ready to order.

   _____

E. Using indirect speech, rewrite what Felix said.

We'll have a game with Harry's team tomorrow but we haven't quite prepared yet because a lot of my teammates are still busy with their projects and they do not have time for practice. I think we'll lose.

_____

_____

_____

_____

_____

_____

_____

_____

Clauses

Clauses can be independent or dependent.

An **independent clause** can stand on its own as a sentence with complete meaning.

A **dependent clause** cannot stand on its own and needs an independent clause to make its meaning complete.

Example: While we were waiting for the bus, it started to rain.
                    (dependent clause)   (independent clause)

A. **Decide if the underlined clause in each of the following sentences is an independent or a dependent clause. Write "IND" for an independent clause and "D" for a dependent clause.**

1. Although it was late, <u>they continued to work on the project</u>. _____

2. Wherever she goes, <u>she carries her doll with her</u>. _____

3. <u>As I was going home</u>, I saw Beth's little cousin. _____

4. <u>If she asked more politely</u>, I would agree to help. _____

5. <u>They gave up</u> because there was too little time. _____

6. <u>However hard they tried</u>, they would not make it. _____

7. <u>I would definitely go with you</u> if I knew he was there. _____

8. Because the weather was bad, <u>we cancelled the trip</u>. _____

9. <u>If you want to succeed</u>, you must put in effort and persevere. _____

10. When the results were announced, <u>the audience booed and yelled</u>. _____

11. It was a pleasant journey <u>although we had to go without her</u>. _____

12. <u>She walks her dog</u> when she has nothing better to do. _____

ISBN: 978-1-897457-06-1

B. Add a dependent clause to each of the following sentences. Write the new sentence on the line.

1. His father was very pleased.

   _____

2. He did not show up.

   _____

3. There was an uproar.

   _____

4. She would not give in.

   _____

5. They took the shortcut.

   _____

6. I will make a deal with you.

   _____

C. Add an independent clause to each of the following sentences.

1. Whenever I am free, _____ .

2. As they were chatting, _____ .

3. Although the two of us have never met before, _____

   _____ .

4. _____

   _____

   wherever he goes.

5. _____

   _____

   because they lost their way.

Compound, Complex, and Compound-Complex Sentences

A **compound sentence** is made up of two or more independent clauses connected by conjunctions.

Example: We looked up the sky and there were countless stars.

A **complex sentence** is made up of an independent clause with at least one dependent clause. A dependent clause is one that is not complete in meaning and has to depend on another clause to make the meaning complete.

Example: Although it was raining, the game continued.
       (dependent clause)   (independent clause)

A **compound-complex sentence** is made up of at least two independent clauses and at least one dependent clause.

Example: If you miss the bus, <u>you will have to walk to school</u> and <u>you will be late</u>.
  (dependent clause)   (independent clause)   (independent clause)

D. State whether each of the following sentences is a compound (C), complex (CX), or compound-complex (CCX) sentence.

1. The children could go to the zoo or they could have a picnic on the beach. _____

2. Mrs. Wilson put the candles on the cake and the children sang the birthday song together. _____

3. When he heard the news, he was thrilled and he ran upstairs to tell his father. _____

4. While I was waiting, I finished reading a very good book. _____

5. If it rains, we will not go to the ball park but we can watch a video at Jason's home. _____

6. Wherever she goes, Rosa always makes friends because she is such a kind person. _____

7. Although she didn't tell me, I knew that there was something wrong. _____

ISBN: 978-1-897457-06-1

E. Add an independent clause to each of the following sentences to make it a compound sentence.

1. They arrived early but _____ .

2. We can start all over again or _____ .

3. The waitress did not say a word and _____ .

4. The players were disgruntled but _____ .

5. It was a sunny day and _____ .

F. Add a dependent or an independent clause to each of the following sentences to make it a complex sentence.

1. We were told to stay indoor _____
_____ .

2. Although no one won the bonus prize, _____
_____ .

3. While the girls were packing in the room, _____
_____ .

4. I will go ahead with the project _____
_____ .

G. Write a compound-complex sentence.

_____
_____
_____
_____

ISBN: 978-1-897457-06-1

A. Read the story. For each underlined word, write which part of speech it is in the parentheses: noun, pronoun, verb, adjective, adverb, preposition, conjunction, or interjection.

As part of her summer <u>vacation</u> (1. _____), Rachel travelled <u>from</u>

(2. _____) Ottawa, Canada to Cushendall, Ireland. She stayed with

her Aunt Anne and Uncle Pat for three weeks. They <u>lived</u> (3. _____) in

a large house on a big property in the <u>rolling</u> (4. _____) countryside. <u>It</u>

(5. _____) was her first time in Ireland and she didn't know what to

expect.

When Rachel first arrived, she was fascinated by how green everything was.

"<u>Wow</u> (6. _____)!" she said. "This place is so beautiful!" It was a warm

and <u>sunny</u> (7. _____) day. Rachel was eager to play outside <u>but</u>

(8. _____) her aunt told her she needed to unpack her things <u>neatly</u>

(9. _____) first.

She <u>met</u> (10. _____) Murphy, her aunt and uncle's golden retriever.

He is a <u>friendly</u> (11. _____) dog. After Rachel finished unpacking, <u>she</u>

(12. _____) played with Murphy outside <u>in</u> (13. _____) the grass

for most of the afternoon.

ISBN: 978-1-897457-06-1

B. Rewrite the sentences using a different voice.

1. Rachel and Murphy climbed the hills.

   _____

2. A rustling sound was heard by Rachel.

   _____

3. An old tree stump was discovered by Murphy.

   _____

4. Murphy sniffed the grass behind the tree stump.

   _____

   _____

5. The dog was called by Rachel.

   _____

   _____

6. Rachel's call was ignored by Murphy.

   _____

   _____

C. Write the numbers in the boxes to tell which mood the underlined sentences are written in.

Rachel tried whistling but that didn't work either. "1. Come here, Murphy!" Rachel yelled. Either Murphy didn't hear her or he was ignoring her. "2. I wish you would listen to me," she said to him. "3. Please listen to me!" she called to Murphy. 4. He wouldn't stop sniffing the grass. Rachel eventually gave up. 5. She walked over to where Murphy was.

Imperative

Indicative

Subjunctive

D. Write "gerund", "participle", or "infinitive" to tell which type of verbal is underlined in each sentence.

1. Rachel went <u>to see</u> what Murphy was interested in. _____

2. He really enjoys <u>digging</u> so she thought that's what he was doing. _____

3. He stood behind a pile of <u>broken</u> branches. _____

4. Rachel wanted <u>to know</u> what he had found. _____

5. She likes <u>learning</u> about new things. _____

6. Behind the pile of branches, Rachel saw something she hadn't expected <u>to find</u>. _____

7. There stood a small man with red hair holding a tiny <u>walking</u> stick! _____

E. Fill in the blanks with the appropriate verbal phrase.

| a torn jacket | to leave the man alone |
| finding a leprechaun |
| making your wishes | the barking dog |

1. The man wore a brown scarf, _____ , and an old hat.

2. The man wasn't afraid of _____ .

3. Rachel was planning _____ until he told her he was a leprechaun.

4. He said to Rachel, "Don't you know that you get three wishes for _____ ?"

5. "But I must tell you," he warned her. "You should think very carefully before _____ ."

ISBN: 978-1-897457-06-1

F. Underline the noun phrase(s) in each sentence.

1. Rachel had never seen such a small and strange looking man.

2. She had always thought leprechauns were imaginary characters.

3. Murphy had stopped barking and his curious expression made Rachel laugh.

4. The leprechaun's name was Seamus and Rachel thought this was a lovely name.

5. Rachel's first wish was an easy decision.

6. She asked Seamus for a giant, gooey cheesecake.

7. Seamus was disappointed with Rachel's wasteful wish.

8. The cake appeared in the grassy, green hills.

9. Rachel started to eat the incredibly delicious treat.

G. Fill in the blanks with the appropriate adjective phrases or adverb phrases.

> in the grass   too quickly   from Canada
>   over the hills   deep front

1. Rachel ate the cake _____ which made her feel sick.

2. Seamus, Rachel, and Murphy lay _____ until Rachel felt better.

3. Seamus asked Rachel where she was from and she said that she was _____ .

4. Rachel placed Seamus in her _____ pocket to take him back to the house.

5. They raced _____ to get home in time.

H. Change the sentences into indirect speech.

1. "You've almost missed dinner!" Aunt Anne exclaimed.

   _____

2. Uncle Pat asked, "Where have you been?"

   _____

3. "I was playing outside with Murphy," explained Rachel.

   _____

4. "Shall we sit down and eat?" asked Aunt Anne.

   _____

5. Rachel said, "I'm not very hungry."

   _____

6. "Why aren't you hungry?" Uncle Pat asked Rachel. "You haven't had
   anything to eat."

   _____

   _____

7. "I'm not feeling well. Can I go to bed?" Rachel asked her aunt and uncle.

   _____

8. Aunt Anne touched Rachel's forehead and said,
   "You don't have a fever."

   _____

   _____

9. "Go ahead," said Uncle Pat. "You can eat later."

   _____

   _____

ISBN: 978-1-897457-06-1

I. **Indicate whether each of the sentences is compound (C), complex (CX), or compound-complex (CCX).**

1. Not only was Rachel not hungry, she also wanted to let Seamus out of her pocket. _____

2. When she got upstairs, she took him out and placed him on the bed. _____

3. She wanted to make another wish but Seamus suggested that she think about it some more. _____

4. Rachel said she had thought about it and that she was sure this was something she wanted. _____

5. Seamus waited for her wish and hoped it wasn't for another cake. _____

6. Although her wish wasn't for a cake, it didn't make Seamus happy. _____

J. **Fill in the blanks with the appropriate independent or dependent clauses.**

> wherever I go   even though Seamus disapproved
> you only have one wish left   she saw it appear out of thin air

1. _____ , Rachel was happy with her second wish.

2. She wished for a new bicycle and _____
_____ .

3. "_____ , this bicycle will come with me!" said Rachel.

4. "_____ so you should make it a good one," said Seamus.

Writing Concise Sentences

Clear and concise writing makes it easy for the reader to understand the ideas we want to convey. Remember these points when writing sentences and paragraphs:

- Separate sentences that contain more than one idea into two.
- Combine short sentences that contain related ideas into one sentence.
- Simplify overloaded sentences by cutting out unnecessary details or descriptions.
- The main idea in all the sentences in a paragraph should be related.

A. Improve the group of sentences below using the above guidance.

1. Jonathan watched a television show about dinosaurs that was very interesting and he wanted to learn more about dinosaurs so he asked his parents to take him to the museum so that he could learn more.

   _____
   _____
   _____

2. Jonathan brought a friend. His friend's name is Matthew. Matthew likes dinosaurs, too. Matthew had never been to the museum before. Matthew was very excited.

   _____
   _____

3. They visited all of the exhibits about dinosaurs. They stopped for lunch in the cafeteria. They were not tired. They visited the exhibits about ancient Egypt after lunch.

   _____
   _____

ISBN: 978-1-897457-06-1

B. Put each group of related ideas below in one sentence.

> Decide on the order of presenting the ideas before writing.

Example: Sarah went to the mall.
                She went to the bookstore.
                She bought a new novel.
                She bought the one her friend recommended to her.

<u>Because her friend recommended the book, Sarah went to the bookstore in the mall and bought the new novel.</u>

1. The Smiths went on a vacation.

   They went to Italy.

   They went to Rome in Italy.

   They stayed there for two weeks.

_____

_____

2. It was Alex's birthday.

   Marjorie came to visit Alex.

   Marjorie brought him a present.

   Marjorie brought him a cake.

_____

_____

3. The cave was pitch dark.

   The cave was eerie.

   The children held their breaths.

   They dared not make a sound.

_____

_____

Faulty Parallels

A **faulty parallel** occurs when the coordinate elements in a sentence do not have a consistent grammatical construction.

Example: We like swimming, fishing, and baseball in the summer. (✗)
              We like swimming, fishing, and playing baseball in the summer. (✔)

C. Rewrite the following sentences to correct the faulty parallels.

1. My sister always wants to get the lead role and becoming famous.

    _____

    _____

2. Weight gain is often the result of eating too much candy, junk food, and eating between meals.

    _____

    _____

3. They think science projects are more interesting than English.

    _____

    _____

4. It is important to work hard and doing well in school.

    _____

    _____

5. Her success was due to her perseverance, hard work, and she was getting support from her family.

    _____

    _____

ISBN: 978-1-897457-06-1

Dangling Modifiers

To avoid confusion in meaning, we need to keep the modifier close to the words it modifies.

Example: He saw an old building walking into an alley. (✘)
(The sentence seems to say that an old building was walking into an alley.)
Walking into an alley, he saw an old building. (✔)

D. Rewrite the following sentences to correct the dangling and misplaced modifiers.

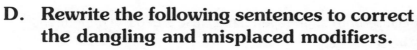 

You may change the order of the words or add new words.

1. They specially baked a huge birthday cake for her.

   _____

   _____

2. The undercover police officer caught the pickpocket posing as a tourist.

   _____

   _____

3. My father almost earned two thousand dollars more for the additional work.

   _____

   _____

4. She read the story about Little Ann with her sister.

   _____

   _____

5. He caught sight of a spider talking to his mother.

   _____

   _____

unit 8 Punctuation (1)

Commas

We use a **comma** to:

- separate words or phrases in a series.

  Example: I enjoy playing hockey, baseball, and basketball.

- separate adjectives before a noun.

  Example: She wore a long, satin dress to the party.

- separate a dependent clause from an independent clause when the dependent clause appears first in the sentence.

  Example: When they heard the news, they broke into tears.

- set off transitional words.

  Example: However, I ignored him and continued with my work.

- set off a direct quotation.

  Example: Jeremy said to him, "You'd better finish it on time."

- set off words in apposition.

  Example: Our teacher, Mr. Weir, will teach at another school next term.

A. Add commas where needed in the following sentences.

1. The farmer gave us some carrots, a few apples, and a lot of potatoes.

2. Did you see the sleek, blue sports car, on the driveway?

3. Mrs. Thomson, our next door neighbour, told us not to worry.

4. Once we start, we should continue and not give up.

5. Although I didn't see it happen, I could feel the horror.

6. The little boy replied, "I just asked for some candies."

7. Indeed, it was the best we could do for her.

8. The incident happened on June 19, 2004.

9. The storm left the village, with flooded basements, fallen trees, and mudslides.

 ISBN: 978-1-897457-06-1

Using Commas to Set off Non-defining Clauses

We use commas to set off a non-defining clause in a sentence. A non-defining clause is one that adds information but is not a necessary part of the sentence.

Example: The coach, <u>who is a native of Windsor</u>, doesn't think that they stand a chance in the play-off.

We do not use commas to set off a defining clause because a defining clause is essential to defining the noun described.

Example: I need the book <u>that explains weather and climate</u> to complete the project.

B. Decide which of the following sentences contain non-defining clauses. Add commas where needed.

1. Our dog which everyone loves likes eating snacks.

2. The show that he wanted to watch was not telecast.

3. The teachers who play in the game will practise tomorrow at the gym.

4. On my way to school, I ran into Jim's mother who told me that Jim was not feeling well.

5. Don't you want to be someone that everybody admires?

6. She let me see her camera which was as thin as a credit card.

7. I know a place where we can play hide-and-seek.

8. Never trust a stranger who offers you a ride home.

9. He is a player whom everyone looks up to.

10. The tools that we need for the repair work are stored in the shed over there.

11. Pam's younger sister who looks very much like her will come to the party too.

12. Mrs. Steele whose son is about my age bakes great cookies.

Colons

We use a **colon**:
- to introduce a list of items or a quotation.

  Example: There are three main ingredients in lemon squares: lemon juice, sugar, and flour.

- to set off a concluding statement.

  Example: When you are travelling, remember one thing: home is where the heart is.

- between a title and a subtitle.

  Example: The writers agreed that "The Best Word: The Art of Writing Well" was worth a second read.

- between two clauses when the second one explains the first.

  Example: There are two ways you can get to the island: you can take a boat or you can take an airplane.

C. Add colons where needed in the following sentences.

1. The chairman neglected one crucial fact the report was not ready.

2. The article "Travel in Asia China and India" is an interesting read.

3. We expect only one thing from him complete the project by next Monday.

4. They were told to pack these for the trip a flashlight, a compass, and a radio.

5. The company had the following openings secretary, receptionist, administrative assistant.

6. We all have the same goal win the tournament this time.

7. The old saying goes "Blood is thicker than water."

8. Do remember this never ever give up.

ISBN: 978-1-897457-06-1

Semicolons

We use a **semicolon**:
- in place of a conjunction to join two closely related clauses or sentences.
  Example:　It is raining today; we will go to the zoo another day.

- between a series of items when the items are long or contain commas within.
  Example:　Danielle has three favourite books: The Secret Garden; The Lion, The Witch, and the Wardrobe; The Witches.

D. Add semicolons where needed in the following sentences.

1. To prepare himself for the race, he performed the following exercises every day: weightlifting, which built his upper body strength running, which built up his endurance biking, which strengthened his leg muscles.

2. They met with John it was a brief meeting.

3. He was introduced to the following people: Jason, Peter's cousin Mandy, his boss's daughter Sam, the secretary's husband.

4. It was chilly out there the temperature dropped to a mere 2°C.

5. We tried our best to finish it on time however, we couldn't make it.

6. She's such a popular athlete wherever she goes, she's surrounded by fans.

7. He found himself face to face with someone he knew it was Corey.

8. The surprise gift finally arrived it was a nifty DVD player.

9. No one wanted to leave they were all eager for the announcement.

10. We had a sumptuous dinner everyone was full.

Dashes

We use a **dash** to:

- separate a series at the beginning of a sentence from its explanatory section.

    Example: A compass, a radio, and a flashlight – these are the essentials we need for our hike.

- set off a description or comment that is meant to further the reader's understanding of the sentence.

    Example: The science project – the most difficult of all – will account for 40% of the total score.

- set off an elaboration of an idea at the end of a sentence.

    Example: They had only one thing in mind – winning the game.

A. Rewrite the following sentences, adding dashes where needed.

1.   The final showdown the do-or-die game will be telecast live.

    _____

2.   Everything boiled down to one word perseverance.

    _____

3.   The Greatest Game Ever Played the story of an underdog golfer is the best motivational film I have ever watched.

    _____

    _____

4.   No matter what you do explaining, pleading, or begging it won't make her change her mind.

    _____

    _____

    _____

   ISBN: 978-1-897457-06-1

Hyphens

We use a **hyphen** to join compound words, divide a word into syllables, or indicate a split in a word at the end of the line.

Examples: Compound adjectives: a well-liked teacher, a larger-than-life figure
Compound numbers: fifty-five, one-fifth
Prefixes: anti-social, re-sign (to sign again, as opposed to "resign")

B.   Rewrite the following sentences, adding hyphens where needed.

1.   The new manager is a twenty three year old graduate.

_____

2.   This is a once in a lifetime chance that you shouldn't miss.

_____

3.   Non members are not allowed to go in the members only lounge.

_____

4.   The semi final for the above eighteen contestants will start next week.

_____

5.   He lives in a twenty five year old split level bungalow.

_____

6.   A lot of people were inspired by his from rags to riches story.

_____

_____

7.   The report shows that two thirds of the population are under fifty five years of age.

_____

_____

_____

Parentheses

We use **parentheses** to enclose additional information.

Example: The Mennonites (with a dwindling population) settle mostly in St. Jacobs Country, Ontario.

Parentheses may also be used to add a comment to a statement.

Example: California (see Figure 2) is a state along the Pacific Ocean.

We can also use parentheses to show letters and numbers that designate a series of items.

Example: Before leaving, remember to (a) switch off all the lights, (b) close all the windows, and (c) lock the door.

C. Place parentheses where needed in the following sentences.

1. The new museum see inset will be officially opened on August 21, 2009.

2. The honour students of which I am one are invited to the ceremony.

3. The complimentary tickets a pair from Uncle Charlie and another pair from Mr. Todd came just in time.

4. They should a get a form, b fill it out, c get their parents' consent, and d return it to their teacher before noon tomorrow.

5. The merger yet to be confirmed is said to take effect in January 2010.

6. The graph Fig. 2b shows the population growth over the past 20 years.

7. The series 2-2 would be decided in the final game to be played this afternoon.

8. The supporting role Captain Truman was given to a little-known actor by the name of Willie Whitt.

ISBN: 978-1-897457-06-1

Ellipsis Dots

We use **ellipsis dots** to shorten a quotation when the quotation is longer than what we need.

Example: It is stated clearly in Clause 3: "...with the consent of the director and three board members."

D. Add ellipsis dots with "∧" where needed in the following sentences.

1. Recent research indicates that most of the asteroids orbit around the chance that an asteroid strikes the Earth is one in a million.

2. Malls sprout up in big cities due to the largest shopping centre in the world is the West Edmonton Mall in Edmonton.

3. Malawi is an impoverished third world country in Africa. The infant mortality rate the average life expectancy is only 37 years.

4. There are many ways to conserve energy with more and more people switching to driving smaller cars which are more fuel-efficient.

5. Roberta Bondar became the first female astronaut to go into space. She received the Order of Canada in 1998, Roberta was named to the Canadian Medical Hall of Fame.

6. The cell phone has become almost an indispensable gadget the government is beginning to look into regulating the use of the cell phone.

7. A Great White ranges from five to seven metres in length and weighs swimming at a speed of 16 to 20 km per hour, the Great White usually attacks its prey from behind or beneath.

Root Words, Prefixes, and Suffixes

> **Root Words**
>
> A **root word** is the basic word from which other words are derived.
>
> *Example*:　　agree (root word)
> 　　　　　　　disagree (antonym)
> 　　　　　　　agreeable (adjective)
> 　　　　　　　agreement (noun)

A. Build derivative words from the following root words.

1. able (antonym) _____ (noun) _____

2. tolerate (adjective) _____ (noun) _____

3. quick (verb) _____ (adverb) _____

4. fertile (antonym) _____ (noun) _____

5. formal (antonym) _____ (noun) _____

6. successful (antonym) _____ (noun) _____

B. Identify the root word for each of the following words. Write it on the line provided.

1. discovery _____
2. seemingly _____
3. division _____
4. probability _____
5. monumental _____
6. adventurous _____
7. activity _____
8. extraordinarily _____
9. unsatisfactorily _____
10. sportsmanship _____

ISBN: 978-1-897457-06-1

Prefixes

We can form new words by adding **prefixes** to the beginning of words. These are some common prefixes:

in, im, un, anti, dis – opposites
pro – in favour of; for
out – better than, greater than, separate from
mis – wrong
pre – before; at a previous time
hyper – more than usual
sub – below

C. Use the prefixes above to make new words.

1. merged (went below) _____

2. smart (be smarter than) _____

3. government (against the government) _____

4. satisfied (not satisfied) _____

5. dawn (before dawn) _____

6. possible (not possible) _____

7. understand (understand wrongly) _____

8. number (has a greater number than) _____

9. calculate (calculate wrongly)

_____

10. active (too active)

_____

11. fit (not fit)

_____

Accountant

ISBN: 978-1-897457-06-1

Suffixes

We can also form new words by adding **suffixes** to the end of words. These are some common suffixes:

ful – full of   ness – state of being
able – able to do   al – relating to
ly – in a manner of   ize – to make
less – without   ive – tending to

D. Use the suffixes above to create derivatives.

1. full of thanks   _____

2. in a light manner   _____

3. without a clue   _____

4. tending to respond   _____

5. to make into categories   _____

6. relating to logic   _____

7. able to be paid   _____

8. state of being dark   _____

9. in a strong manner   _____

10. to make real   _____

ISBN: 978-1-897457-06-1

E. **Add suitable prefixes or suffixes to the root words to complete the sentences.**

-ness   im-   -ly   -ize   dis-   sub-

1. Many teachers (approve) _____ of passing notes in class.

2. Maria (quick) _____ walked to the park to meet her friends.

3. The (strange) _____ of the situation bothered Charlie.

4. Dianne needed to wear a very warm coat because of the (zero) _____ temperatures.

5. After waiting for over an hour for his appointment, Jack started to get (patient) _____ .

6. Seamus always wanted to visit Germany and he would often (fantasy) _____ about taking a trip there.

F. **Using prefixes and suffixes, build two derivative words for each of the given words.**

1. help _____ ; _____

2. true _____ ; _____

3. love _____ ; _____

4. do _____ ; _____

5. behave _____ ; _____

6. definite _____ ; _____

7. honest _____ ; _____

8. direct _____ ; _____

unit 11 Homonyms, Synonyms, and Antonyms

> ### Homonyms
>
> **Homonyms** are words that sound alike but have different spellings and meanings. These words are often confused when we create sentences.
>
> *Example*: Kurt was hungry so he ate a <u>pear</u> and an apple. (✔)
>
> Kurt was hungry so he ate a <u>pair</u> and an apple. (✘)

A. Circle the word that suits the meaning of the sentence in each of the following sentences.

1. He helped his teacher pour / pore the liquid into the test tube.

2. I don't think this puppy is theirs / there's .

3. Do you like eating muscles / mussels ?

4. They are having a garage sale to cell / sell the things they don't need.

5. She wanted to find out whether / weather or not the bag was hers.

B. Use the clues to find the homonym pairs.

1. what a clock shows _____

   a herb used in cooking _____

2. run away _____

   a very small insect _____

3. he wears armour _____

   when it gets dark _____

4. rough to touch _____

   where golf is played _____

   ISBN: 978-1-897457-06-1

C. Read the clues and complete the crossword puzzle with homonyms of the words in parentheses.

Across

A. large branch (bow)

B. after third (forth)

C. street (rode)

D. head of school (principle)

E. part of the body (waste)

F. an unwanted plant (we'd)

G. a price to pay (fair)

Down

1. differ (very)

2. amazing act (feet)

3. suffering (pane)

4. person who pays for food and lodgings (border)

5. location (wear)

6. rooms (sweets)

7. given by the sun (raise)

ISBN: 978-1-897457-06-1

> ### Synonyms and Antonyms
>
> A **synonym** is a word that means the same as another word.
>
> *Example*:   lofty – high
>
> An **antonym** is a word that is opposite in meaning to another word.
>
> *Example*:   simple – sophisticated

D.   Read the following sentences.   Suggest a synonym for each of the words in parentheses.

1.   Brandon was (furious) _____ that his brother took his hockey stick.

2.   She felt (humiliated) _____ when she didn't win the award.

3.   My mother was (happy) _____ to go to their anniversary party.

4.   His socks and shoes were (drenched) _____ after he had stepped in the puddle.

5.   It was a (grave) _____ mistake that Matt had made.

6.   I think this is a (touchy) _____ issue that is best left for the manager to decide.

7.   It was a (cold) _____ December evening and everyone on the street (shook) _____ in the winter wind.

8.   Holly was (tired) _____ from staying up so late.

9.   The haunted house was (terrifying) _____ and none of the children were (brave) _____ enough to go inside.

ISBN: 978-1-897457-06-1

E. Rewrite each sentence using an antonym for the word in parentheses.

1. The naughty boy climbed up the tall tree with (difficulty).

   _____

   _____

2. The ballerina danced (clumsily) and earned thunderous applause.

   _____

3. Two beavers were swimming in the (clear) water.

   _____

4. The town became (prosperous) after the Gold Rush.

   _____

5. We strolled leisurely down the (hectic) road.

   _____

6. Marie (whispered) loudly on the roller-coaster ride.

   _____

7. The rumblings from the machine are (pleasing).

   _____

8. Keith is a cheerful and (solitary) boy.

   _____

9. Mr. Moore cannot fall asleep unless the room is completely (bright).

   _____

10. He couldn't remove the writing because he had used a (temporary) marker.

   _____

Troubleshooting Confusing Writing

Pronouns and Possessive Adjectives

Sometimes it is the use of pronouns or possessive adjectives that leads to confusion.

Example: When Kate saw Joanne, she greeted her.
(We do not know who greeted whom.)
When Kate saw Joanne, Kate greeted her.

A. Rewrite the following sentences to remove the confusion.

1. Andrew asked Peter to explain his problem.

_____

2. Ian and Joe worked on a puzzle and he finished it first.

_____

3. The girls in grade six competed against the boys and they lost.

_____

4. Rob met Sam when he first joined the school team.

_____

5. Matt argued with Paul and he was furious.

_____

6. Janice told her best friend Mandy that she had won the first prize.

_____

_____

7. The Jays and the Yankees each scored a run in the seventh inning, and they were confident that they would tie the game soon.

_____

_____

ISBN: 978-1-897457-06-1

Word Order

Sometimes it is the word order that confuses the reader.

Example: Being the youngest child in the family, everyone takes good care of Jim. (It appears as if "everyone" is the youngest child in the family, not Jim.) Jim being the youngest child in the family, everyone takes good care of him.

Or: Being the youngest child in the family, Jim is taken good care of by everyone.

B. Change the word order in the following sentences to correct the confusion.

1. He talked endlessly about his exciting trip last Sunday.

    _____

2. She almost spent all of her savings. Now she is poor.

    _____

3. He told his family about his brush with death after he was rescued.

    _____

4. Being the youngest in the family, no one listens to Mike.

    _____

5. Laughing out loud, the naughty monkey entertained the children.

    _____

6. He saw Ashley and her dog walking to school.

    _____

    _____

7. The children spotted a big fish standing on the riverbank.

    _____

    _____

Subject-Verb Agreement

When putting together a sentence, we need to make sure that the words correspond in both person and number, or "agree" with one another.

Examples: The functions of this nifty MP3 player is listed on the manual. (✗)
The function<u>s</u> of this nifty MP3 player <u>are</u> listed on the manual. (✔)
Marilyn, Sue, and I am going on the trip together. (✗)
Marilyn, Sue, and I <u>are</u> going on the trip together. (✔)
Neither the passengers nor the driver were aware of it. (✗)
Neither the passengers nor the driver <u>was</u> aware of it. (✔)

C. Circle the correct choice in each of the following sentences.

1. Everyone like / likes the model we built.

2. There is / are just a few cookies left.

3. Mr. Simmons, together with all his students, is / are going to sing at the concert.

4. Neither the waiters nor the chef know / knows what's going on.

5. Each / All of them are happy to hear about their sister's success.

6. Anybody who spell / spells the words correctly will be given a prize.

7. Both you and I are / am held responsible for the wrongdoing.

8. Either the workmen or the supervisor was / were at fault.

9. I don't think anyone in class practise / practises it every day.

10. The children, except Ron, has / have agreed to work on it.

11. One / Some of the ingredients is not really that suitable.

12. One / Several of the windows have been broken.

ISBN: 978-1-897457-06-1

D. Read the following sentences. Rewrite those containing faulty agreements.

1. The cell phone with all the bells and whistles comes with a hefty price.

   _____

2. Either you or I are eligible for the scholarship.

   _____

3. The coach, as well as the players, were very disappointed with the decision.

   _____

4. Each of the children were given a basket of strawberries.

   _____

5. No one seems to pay any attention to the performance.

   _____

6. Neither the class nor the teacher have heard of the news.

   _____

7. None of the committee members were prepared to vote.

   _____

8. Have any one of you met our new principal before?

   _____

9. Neither of them was brave enough to take up the challenge.

   _____

10. Someone holding three parcels at the door want to talk to you.

    _____

11. Everyone attending the wedding ceremony were happy for them.

    _____

Inverting Word Order

Inverting the order of the words in a sentence can give it a fresh look and make it more interesting.

Example: The geese flew in unison across the blue sky.
Across the blue sky the geese flew in unison.
Or: In unison across the blue sky flew the geese.

A. Invert the word order in the following sentences to make them sound more interesting.

1.   A crimson sun set over the plain.

   _____

2.   The players assembled in the locker room for a pep talk.

   _____

3.   What she wanted to eat was fish and chips.

   _____

4.   He moved deftly to the side to avoid the tag.

   _____

5.   The firefighters raced against time to save her from the flood.

   _____

6.   The motorbike sped through the narrow alley.

   _____

7.   He scored the winning run with two out and one on third base.

   _____

8.   The kites flew gracefully in the breeze.

   _____

Adding Details

Adding details and descriptive language is another way of making sentences interesting.

Examples: We played on the beach.
We built sandcastles on the quiet, beautiful beach.
They had a game of baseball.
They played an exciting game of baseball after school.

B. Add details to the following sentences. Use additional phrases and clauses where necessary.

1. They went on a trip.

   _____

2. The snow began to fall.

   _____

3. We watched the show.

   _____

4. Fall is a beautiful season.

   _____

5. The bus was full.

   _____

6. The boat sailed on the waterway.

   _____

C. Expand what Michael says in three different ways.

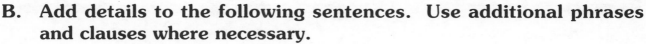

The ride is exciting!

1. _____

   _____

2. _____

3. _____

Descriptive Language

Using **descriptive language** will make your writing more interesting. With each word that you write, make sure you use the best word possible to describe what you want to communicate.

Example: The squirrel ran away when it saw the dog.
                     The tiny squirrel scurried off when he spotted the large, ferocious dog.

D.   For each sentence, replace the underlined word with a more descriptive word from the list of words provided.

inexperienced   considerate   towering   petrified   drained

1.   Donna was <u>scared</u> (   ) to go inside the haunted house.

2.   Mrs. Curtis was <u>tired</u> (   ) from working so much.

3.   Everyone likes him because he is <u>nice</u> (   ).

4.   Jared was too <u>young</u> (   ) to understand the situation.

5.   The <u>tall</u> (   ) cliff appears to be rising straight out of the sea.

E.   Rewrite the sentences. Add or change words to make them more descriptive.

1.   The children ate the melon.

     _____

2.   Iris found a leprechaun in her backyard.

     _____

3.   Hank played his guitar.

     _____

4.   The Carters went to the park on Sunday.

     _____

Wordiness

Wordiness means using more words than necessary. This can cause confusion about the meaning. Clear and concise writing is important for effective communication.

Example: The reason that the road that you need to take to get to my house is so long is due to the fact that it winds. (wordy)

The road to my house is long because it winds. (concise)

F. Rewrite the following sentences in a more concise way.

1. The girls have the ability to ski but the girls would rather not.

   _____

2. In my opinion, I don't think it is proper to do that.

   _____

3. Mother said that it was necessary that we come home for dinner.

   _____

4. The fact is that she doesn't seem to realize the crux of the problem.

   _____

5. In actual fact, they were all eager to take part in it.

   _____

6. The ferry that people take to get to the city of Charlottetown starts here.

   _____

7. We finish school at 3:30 p.m. in the afternoon.

   _____

   _____

8. It occurs to me that I may be late if I don't hurry.

   _____

   _____

A. Read the story. Add punctuation where necessary using commas, colons, semicolons, and dashes.

Rachel was very excited about her shiny red bicycle she had never owned a bicycle before. "I can't wait to take it into town tomorrow!" Rachel exclaimed. "There are three places I really want to go to the library the bakery and the toy store."

"I think that you are forgetting something" said Seamus. Rachel looked at him strangely. She couldn't imagine what he meant.

"Oh! Thank you Seamus for the cake and the bike!" she said.

"You're welcome but that's not what I mean" he said. Don't you think your aunt and uncle are going to wonder where this bicycle came from?"

"I guess I will tell them about finding you" said Rachel.

"I don't think that's a good idea" said Seamus. "They can't see me only children can see me. If you tell them about me they might think there is something wrong with you."

"I know what to do! I'll bring it outside when they are asleep. I will hide it somewhere on the property" said Rachel.

Seamus didn't think this was a good idea but he did not want to argue. He went to sleep in the shoebox Rachel had put out for him. Rachel stayed awake until she heard her aunt and uncle go to bed.

ISBN: 978-1-897457-06-1

B. Rewrite the sentences using dashes, hyphens, and parentheses where appropriate.

1. Rachel slowly carried the bicycle down the twenty six stairs.

   _____

   _____

2. She noticed a shed her uncle built it five years ago which looked old and rickety.

   _____

   _____

3. Rachel thought of many different places the shed, the ditch, and even Murphy's doghouse but she settled on hiding it inside some bushes.

   _____

   _____

4. Morning finally came the moment she had been waiting for and Rachel got ready to go out and ride her bicycle.

   _____

   _____

5. She thought of Fiona Rachel's best friend who has a bicycle just like this one.

   _____

6. Fiona is an eleven year old girl.

   _____

7. It didn't matter to Rachel what the weather was like rainy, foggy, or windy she wasn't going to let anything stop her from riding her bicycle.

   _____

   _____

ISBN: 978-1-897457-06-1

C. Add the suitable prefix or suffix to the root word in each sentence.

> in   able   ly   ive   sub   un   less

1. Rachel (quick) _____ got on the bicycle.

2. Seamus was (comfort) _____ in her front pocket.

3. Murphy was very (respond) _____ and obeyed Rachel.

4. Rachel loved riding the bicycle so much she took (direct) _____ routes to her locations so that she could ride for longer.

5. At the library, Rachel read an article about potatoes that had a (title) _____ of "The Apples of the Earth".

6. Rachel had been (care) _____ and had forgotten to lock up her bicycle.

7. While she browsed through the books inside the library, she was (aware) _____ that someone was taking her bicycle.

D. Identify the root word for each of the underlined words.

1. Murphy had fallen asleep while waiting for Rachel outside the library, so he was <u>unconscious</u> ( ) when the bicycle was stolen.

2. Rachel was in <u>disbelief</u> ( ) when she saw her bicycle gone.

3. "This is <u>unbelievable</u> ( )!" said Rachel.

4. "You should have locked your bicycle as a <u>precaution</u> ( )," said Seamus.

5. "It must be some kind of <u>misunderstanding</u> ( )," Rachel said.

E. Circle the appropriate word in each homonym pair to complete the sentence.

1. "We should ask people if they saw the root / route the thief took," said Rachel.

2. They asked a few people but no one seemed to know who it was or which way / weigh the thief went.

3. "Look!" said Rachel. "I've found a piece / peace of material! Maybe this belongs to the thief!"

4. "That won't help you figure out the thief's coarse / course ," Seamus said.

5. "I still have one / won wish left, don't I?" asked Rachel.

6. "That's write / right ," said Seamus. "But you should make sure you use it wisely."

F. Fill in the blank with a synonym for each of the words in parentheses.

1. Rachel (thought) _____ about her last wish for a while.

2. Seamus was (anxiously) _____ waiting to hear what she would say.

3. "I really want to know who (took) _____ my bicycle," Rachel said.

4. Seamus asked, "Is that your (last) _____ wish?"

5. Rachel thought about it one last time and told Seamus, "Yes, I am (sure) _____ that is what I want my last wish to be."

G. Circle the word that is an antonym of the underlined word.

Seamus was not very <u>unhappy</u> [1. thrilled / pleased] with Rachel's decision. Even though he did not like it, Seamus must grant Rachel's wish. Rachel <u>dropped</u> [2. lifted / pushed] Seamus into her pocket. She looked <u>up</u> [3. down / beside] at him. "Aren't you going to tell me who did it?" she asked.

"I can't tell you," he said. "You will find out soon enough."

Rachel sat on the stairs leading to the library. Then she decided to walk to the bakery. She looked <u>carelessly</u> [4. closely / carefully] at every bicycle on her way there but none were hers. Murphy walked <u>quickly</u> [5. slowly / sadly] beside Rachel. He seemed to feel bad about being <u>awake</u> [6. asleep / tired] when the bicycle was stolen.

H. Fill in the blanks with the correct forms of the verbs so that the verbs agree with the subjects. Use the present tense.

> begin   arrive   see   walk   walk   be   be   sit

1. Rachel and Murphy _____ to the bakery.

2. Rachel _____ quickly.

3. Seamus _____ in Rachel's pocket.

4. It _____ to rain just as they _____ at the bakery.

5. The bakery _____ very busy.

6. Rachel and Murphy _____ not hungry.

7. Rachel _____ a red bike outside and a little boy standing next to it.

ISBN: 978-1-897457-06-1

I. Change the word in parentheses to one of the more descriptive words.

> glared   explained   astonished   glimmering   stole

1. Rachel was certain that the (shiny) _____ red bicycle was hers.

2. She approached the boy and (looked) _____ at him.

3. "Hey, you (took) _____ my bicycle!" she said.

4. "This bicycle belongs to me," the boy said, (surprised) _____ by how Rachel had spoken to him.

5. He (said) _____ that his bicycle went missing the day before and that he found it that day at the library.

J. Rewrite the sentences to make them less wordy.

1. Rachel was a bit confused and puzzled about the bicycle due to the fact that she thought Seamus had given her that bicycle.

_____

_____

2. Seamus told Rachel that the bicycle was taken for the reason that bicycles did not just appear out of nowhere.

_____

_____

3. At this point in time, Rachel now understood that she should have been more careful with her wishes.

_____

_____

Grammar Summary

Parts of Speech

There are eight **parts of speech** in English: noun, pronoun, verb, adjective, adverb, preposition, conjunction, and interjection.

Verbs

The **verb** tells us the tense, voice, and mood of the sentence.

The **tense** tells us when an action occurred or will occur.

The **voice** shows the relationship between the verb and the subject. The voice can be active or passive. The **active voice** shows that the subject is doing the action whereas the **passive voice** shows that the subject is receiving the action.

The **mood** tells us in what manner the verb is communicating the action. The mood can be indicative, imperative, or subjunctive. The **indicative mood** makes a basic statement or asks a question. The **imperative mood** makes a command or request. The **subjunctive mood** indicates a wish, a hypothetical case, a suggestion, or a demand.

Verbals

Verbals are formed from verbs but function as nouns, adjectives, or adverbs. There are three types of verbals: gerunds, participles, and infinitives.

Gerunds end in "ing" and function as nouns.

Participles are verbals that are used as adjectives.

Infinitives are the "to" form of verbs. They can be nouns, adjectives, or adverbs.

Phrases

A **phrase** is a group of words that has no subject or predicate.

A **noun phrase** is made up of a noun and all its modifiers.

An **adjective phrase** describes a noun.

An **adverb phrase** describes a verb.

Many adjective phrases and adverb phrases are introduced by prepositions.

A **verbal phrase** contains a gerund, a participle, or an infinitive. It functions as a noun, an adjective, or an adverb.

ISBN: 978-1-897457-06-1

Direct and Indirect Speech

Direct speech repeats the exact words spoken and these words are put in between quotation marks.

Indirect speech reports what someone else said and no quotation marks are needed.

Changing direct speech to indirect speech involves changes in tense, time reference, and pronouns.

Clauses and Sentences

An **independent clause** can stand on its own as a sentence.

A **dependent clause** cannot stand on its own and needs an independent clause to make its meaning complete.

A **compound sentence** is made up of two or more independent clauses connected by conjunctions.

A **complex sentence** is made up of an independent clause with at least one dependent clause.

A **compound-complex sentence** is made up of at least two independent clauses and at least one dependent clause.

Examples

- **Mike took a few photos and he strolled quite leisurely along the sunny beach to search for the rather rare sand dollars.**
  (two independent clauses joined by "and" to form a compound sentence in the simple past tense written in the active voice and indicative mood)

  a few photos; the sunny beach; the rather rare sand dollars – noun phrases

  quite leisurely; along the beach – adverb phrases

  rather rare – adjective phrase

  to search for the rather rare sand dollars – verbal phrase (infinitive phrase)

- <u>Although he didn't find any</u>, <u>Mike said he had a good time</u>.
      (dependent clause)   (independent clause)
  (a complex sentence with an independent clause and a dependent clause)

  Mike said he had a good time – indirect speech

Sentences

Sentences should be concise, each containing either one idea or related ideas.

The coordinate elements in a sentence should be parallel, that is, they should have a consistent grammatical construction.

A modifier should be kept close to the words it modifies to avoid confusion in meaning.

Punctuation

The **comma** separates words or phrases in a series, adjectives before a noun, or a dependent clause from an independent clause when the dependent clause appears first in the sentence. Commas also set off transitional words, direct quotations, words in apposition, or non-defining clauses in a sentence.

The **colon** introduces a list of items or a quotation or sets off a concluding statement. It can be used between a title and a subtitle or between two clauses when the second one explains the first.

The **semicolon** is used in place of a conjunction to join two closely related clauses or sentences. It is also used between a series of items when the items are long or contain commas within.

The **dash** separates a series at the beginning of a sentence from its explanatory section, sets off a description or comment that is meant to further the reader's understanding of the sentence, or sets off an elaboration of an idea at the end of a sentence.

The **hyphen** joins compound words, divides a word into syllables, or indicates a split in a word at the end of a line.

Parentheses enclose additional information, add a comment or statement, or show letters and numbers that designate a series of items.

Ellipsis dots indicate that a quotation has been shortened.

Root Words, Prefixes, and Suffixes

A **root word** is the basic word from which other words are derived.

New words can be formed by adding **prefixes** to the beginning of words or adding **suffixes** to the end of words.

Homonyms, Synonyms, and Antonyms

Homonyms are words that sound alike but have different spellings and meanings.

Synonyms are words that have the same meaning.

Antonyms are words that have opposite meanings.

Troubleshooting Confusing Writing

Pronouns and **possessive adjectives** can lead to confusion. **Word order** can also confuse the reader. Be as clear as possible when writing your sentences.

Every sentence must have **subject-verb agreement**. The words must correspond in both person and number.

Add Colour to Your Writing

There are different ways to make writing more interesting to read. **Inverting word order** in a sentence, **adding details**, and **using descriptive language** are some ways to do so.

Example

- We had to pay an unwelcome, expensive fare to get into the fair – the one located downtown. We went on some thrilling rides: Thunder Dragon, Horror Express, and The Abyss. We ended up in a really boring ghost house.

  unwelcome – formed from the root word "welcome" with the prefix "un"

  expensive – formed from the root word "expense" with the suffix "ive"

  fare; fair – homonyms

  thrilling; boring – antonyms

  commas – separates the adjectives "unwelcome" and "expensive" before the noun "fare"

       – separate the three rides in the list

  dash – sets off the description "the one located downtown" to tell the reader more about the fair

  colon – introduces the list of rides

ISBN: 978-1-897457-06-1

We are cheery birds.

cheery

ISBN: 978-1-897457-06-1

1 Creating an Interesting Story Ending

The Ending of a Story

The ending of a story can be the solution to a problem or conflict or an exciting or interesting event that completes the action of the story.

A. Read the following story and add an ending in the space provided.

Opening
the Cottage

It was the last weekend in May, and it was the time of year that the Fernandez family opened their cottage for the summer season. They always packed the car on Thursday night so that they could get away as early as possible on Friday. They packed warm clothes, sleeping bags, and lots of food. They always had delicious snacks available in the car for the long trip. To pass the time on the long drive, they played cards, trivia games, and their favourite game, "I Spy".

After a four-hour drive on the highway, they arrived at the cottage road. The moon was bright in the dark sky and it shed silver light on the cottage road. Mr. Fernandez drove very slowly along the winding, gravel road. The children had forgotten how scary it was on this dark road. The trees cast eerie shadows across the windshield, and they could hear the noise of animals moving in the bushes along the roadside. Suddenly the headlights shone on a groundhog and it froze in the path of the car. Mr. Fernandez slammed on his brakes, and the frightened animal scurried into the brush.

After much anticipation, they finally arrived at the cottage. It was very dark but Mrs. Fernandez had a flashlight, and the family followed her up to the cottage door. Mr. Fernandez opened the door to the cottage and Mrs. Fernandez reached inside for the light switch. When the lights went on inside the cottage, the family was shocked by what they saw.

ISBN: 978-1-897457-06-1

Ending

____

____

____

____

____

____

____

The Main Idea

B. From the choices below, place a check mark beside the statement that best states the main idea of each paragraph.

Paragraph 1

A. The Fernandez family liked to eat in the car on long road trips. ____

B. The Fernandez family were going to open their cottage for the season. ____

C. The Fernandez cottage was far away. ____

Paragraph 2

A. The cottage road was dark and scary. ____

B. Animals often jumped in front of cars. ____

C. Mr. Fernandez drove slowly along the dark road. ____

Paragraph 3

A. The family saw something shocking in the cottage. ____

B. The cottage had no lights. ____

C. Mrs. Fernandez was the only one with a flashlight. ____

ISBN: 978-1-897457-06-1

Word Study

C. **Find the words in the original story that mean the following.**

1. unimportant information (paragraph 1) _____
2. surprised (paragraph 3) _____
3. strange and frightening (paragraph 2) _____
4. eagerness (paragraph 3) _____
5. bushes (paragraph 2) _____
6. scampered (paragraph 2) _____

Setting and Suspense

Setting refers to the time and the place of a story.
Suspense is what makes the reader eagerly anticipate the ending of a story.

D. **To create suspense, a writer will often use a series of events that lead to the end of the story or descriptions that heighten the reader's interest.**

1. Give details about the setting in this story.

   TIME: _____

   _____

   PLACE: _____

   _____

2. What events and descriptions create suspense in the story? (Try to name two of each.)

   EVENTS: a. _____

   b. _____

   DESCRIPTIONS: a. _____

   b. _____

ISBN: 978-1-897457-06-1

Using Descriptive Language

Descriptive language makes a story more interesting. Adjectives, adverbs, and action verbs create vivid images for the reader.

E. Each sentence below is missing a descriptive word such as an adjective or adverb, or an action word such as a verb. Complete the sentences with appropriate descriptive words from the word bank.

1. The _____ birds _____

   high above the buildings.

2. After eating a _____ meal, the family watched an

   _____ movie.

3. The _____ mountain climb was dangerous

   even for the most _____ climber.

4. The ocean waves _____ against the shore while the

   swimmers _____ to stay afloat.

5. During the last part of the _____

   race, the _____ runner sprinted

   _____ towards the finish line.

6. The church bells _____ loudly in the

   _____ village to announce the Sunday

   service.

tiredly	treacherous	quaint	graceful	exciting
soared	experienced	delicious
struggled	chimed	smashed	marathon	exhausted

2 Clustering Ideas – A Creative Writing Process

Clustering Ideas

A cluster of ideas is a collection of words or phrases that form the basic idea of a story.

A. Below is a cluster of words and phrases that could be the original ideas for a story entitled "A Summer Holiday". Add 10 more words or phrases to this cluster.

A Summer Holiday

	swimming	swimming races
	holiday	lying in the sun
July	cool lake	windy day
big waves	sand	vacation
frisbee	goggles	hot weather
friends	no school	barbecue
sunburn	rocks	canoe
diving	motor boat	fishing

_____

_____

_____

_____

_____

_____

_____

_____

_____

_____

ISBN: 978-1-897457-06-1

B. Compose a brief story developed from the ideas in the cluster.

Use an **introductory** sentence that states what you are writing about. Follow that sentence with the **development** sentences that give the events of your story. End your story with an interesting **conclusion**.

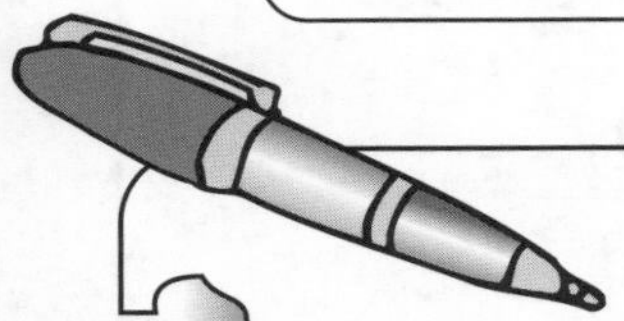

Title: _____

_____

_____

_____

_____

_____

_____

_____

_____

_____

_____

_____

_____

_____

_____

_____

C. **Create a story using a cluster of ideas.**

Choose a topic from the list below.

The Championship Game	Danger at the Zoo
Beware of the Unexpected	Planning a Surprise Party
The School Trip	A Trip to a Foreign Land
A Hero for a Day	Moving Day – Our New House
A Summer in the Country	The Mystery of the Old House
Snowboarding Challenge	Learning about a Foreign Culture
The Pet that Saved a Life	The Dangerous Journey

Fill in the cluster balloons below with words and phrases to suit your topic.

_____

_____

_____

_____

_____

_____

Remember to use adjectives to describe the nouns and adverbs to describe the action words in your sentences. **Action verbs** *peak the reader's interest.*

≪ Introductory Sentence ≫

State the main idea of your story or create interest in what you are writing about.

_____

_____

≪ Story Development Sentences ≫

1. _____

_____

_____

Each sentence advances the storyline and gives details about what is happening.

2. _____

_____

3. _____

_____

4. _____

_____

5. _____

_____

≪ Conclusion ≫

1. _____

_____

2. _____

Create a sentence or two that finishes the action of your story, solves the problem your characters faced, or sums up the main idea.

_____

3 A Way with Words

Confusing Words

Many words sound or look similar but have different meanings.

Example: She was **to** tired **too** go **two** the store.   – INCORRECT
She was **too** tired **to** go **to** the store.   – CORRECT

A. **Choose the correct word to suit the context of each of the sentences below.**

1. He would rather be playing golf _____ going to work.
(then / than)

2. The _____ report called for rain in the
afternoon. (weather / whether)

3. _____ fun to go to the zoo and see
exotic animals. (Its / It's)

4. _____ , up in the tree, sat the neighbour's
cat. (Their / There / They're)

5. He _____ the ball to the
back catcher but the runner was safe.
(threw / through)

6. _____ books were left on the desk at
recess? (Who's / Whose)

7. She was a _____ for sore eyes. (cite / sight / site)

8. The sign read: " _____ , Hospital Zone."
(Quite / Quiet / Quit)

9. The teacher asked, "Did you _____
your pen?" (loose / lose)

10. It was a long _____ for the bus because of a traffic jam.
(weight / wait)

   ISBN: 978-1-897457-06-1

Avoiding Padded Language

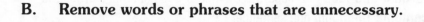

Some words and phrases are unnecessary. Often these words or phrases can be replaced by a single word.

Example: In my opinion I think that it is a good idea.
"In my opinion" is unnecessary because it means the same as "I think".

B.   Remove words or phrases that are unnecessary.

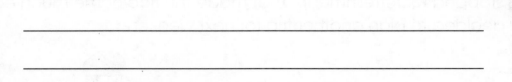

1.   What I believe is that dogs make the best pets.

_____

2.   It was in fact an ideal day for sailing.

_____

3.   What I think is that people should eat more fruits and
     vegetables.

_____

_____

4.   I'm not sure and I might be wrong but I think today is her birthday.

_____

5.   The reason that I didn't go to the movie was that I had already seen it.

_____

_____

6.   What I don't understand is why some people refuse to
     exercise.

_____

_____

7.   It was on account of the fact that he was too young to get a job.

_____

Concise Writing

It is important to be clear and concise in your writing. Follow these steps when composing sentences and paragraphs:

1. Decide what is the **main idea** of each sentence.
2. Look for sentences that contain **more than one idea** and separate them into two sentences or look for short sentences similar in topic and **combine them** into one sentence.
3. Examine each sentence for clarity; write simple sentences that clearly state your main idea.
4. Stay on topic. The main idea in all sentences should be related.

C. **Improve each of these sentences by following the steps above.**

*Some sentences may be **overloaded** while others may need combining.*

1. The weather report called for sunny skies so they decided to go on a long bike ride, besides John wanted to try out his new bike that he received as a birthday gift.

_____

_____

_____

2. John rode a ten-speed bike. Mabel rode a twelve-speed bike.

_____

3. They rode for 5 kilometres and part of the ride was uphill and at the end they were very tired because they were not used to riding uphill.

_____

_____

4. The riders stopped for refreshment. That made the ride home much easier, and they decided to plan another trip for next weekend.

_____

_____

_____

D. Rewrite the sentences below removing unnecessary detail.

1. My teacher, who owns a red car, is very good at explaining the Mathematics programme.

   _____

2. The automobile, which had new tires, was parked in front of the house for two days.

   _____

3. The pitcher, who signed autographs before the game, threw a no-hitter.

   _____

4. They looked at the neighbour's pictures of her trip to Europe because pictures are always interesting.

   _____

   _____

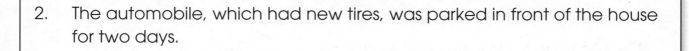

Challenge

Create a single sentence with each group of related ideas below. Choose the order in which the ideas are presented. Use conjunctive adverbs where necessary.

1. she found the lost kitten
   she searched throughout the neighbourhood

   _____

   _____

2. the car broke down
   they were driving to Ottawa
   they were going to visit relatives

   _____

   _____

4 Writing a Factual Composition

People have always been fascinated with the massive size and strange physical features of the elephant. The Asian elephant weighs up to 5,000 kilograms and stands almost 3 metres high; the African elephant is even larger at 7,000 kilograms and 4 metres in height. Their tusks are actually upper incisors and continue to grow throughout their lives. The elephant's floppy ears have numerous blood vessels which give off heat keeping the elephant cool.

Despite their massive size, elephants are actually very gentle. Living in the marshes and river valleys of Southeast Asia, China, and Africa, they spend their day

THE Largest Land Mammal

eating huge quantities of food, as much as 300 kilograms a day, and drinking up to 190 litres of water.

Although the elephant is one of the most loved animals in the animal kingdom, it has become an endangered species due to the destruction of their habitat and because of illegal hunting by poachers who kill elephants for their valuable ivory tusks.

A.   Make a list of 6 facts about the elephant found in the passage above.

1. _____

2. _____

3. _____

4. _____

5. _____

6. _____

ISBN: 978-1-897457-06-1

Organizing Facts

To write a composition using facts, it is important to group the facts and organize them into a logical sequence for presentation.

B. **Below is a list of facts about cheetahs to be used to compose a paragraph. Follow the steps below to create your composition.**

Step One	Read over all the facts in the list.
Step Two	Organize the facts by grouping them according to a common topic (use a number or letter system to group the common facts).
Step Three	Organize the groups of facts in order of presentation in your paragraph. For example, describe the size of the cheetah first.
Step Four	Write an interesting topic sentence to introduce your subject.
Step Five	From your groups of facts, compose interesting sentences; vary the length and structure of each sentence to add variety; add your own descriptive words.
Step Six	Write a concluding sentence that does one of the following: 1. summarizes your topic 2. gives the reader something further to think about

Facts about
Cheetahs

- Cheetah cubs leave the mother when they are 18 months old. _____
- Cheetahs are more effective runners in short bursts. _____
- Cheetahs are carnivorous. _____
- Cheetahs are up to 2 metres in length. _____
- Cheetahs live on grassy plains and in semi-desert areas. _____
- Cheetahs can run up to 110 kilometres per hour. _____
- Cheetahs live for approximately 9 years in the wild. _____
- Cheetahs give birth to between 3 and 5 cubs. _____
- Cheetahs weigh approximately 65 kilograms. _____
- Cheetahs use their speed in short bursts to catch their prey. _____

This can be changed before creating the final copy.

Working Title: _____

Topic Sentence: _____

_____

Use the facts to create sentences; do not be concerned with the order of the sentences at this point.

Body Sentences:

1. _____

_____

_____

2. _____

_____

_____

3. _____

_____

_____

4. _____

_____

_____

5. _____

_____

_____

Concluding Sentence:

_____

_____

C. Follow the steps below to complete your final copy.

Step One **Proofread and Edit**

1. Read over your sentences looking for errors in spelling and grammar. Make sure each sentence is complete with subject and verb.

2. Make changes by adding, removing, or changing words.

Step Two **Arrange Sentences**

Arrange the sentences you have composed into the most logical sequence to get your ideas across in the best way.

Step Three **Topic and Concluding Sentences**

Make sure that your **topic** sentence clearly states your topic and peaks the reader's interest. Check your **concluding** sentence to ensure that it either summarizes your ideas or provides an interesting after-thought to your topic.

Title: _____

_____

_____

_____

_____

_____

_____

_____

_____

_____

_____

_____

_____

_____

_____

5 Creative Sentence Structure – You're the Architect

An architect designs a building with a specific purpose in mind. As a writer, you are an architect of the sentences you compose. You have the choice of arranging words and phrases to suit your meaning or the emphasis you want to express.

A. **Rearrange the words and phrases in each of the sentences below.**

Example: Because we are close friends, I am happy to offer my help.

Could be written as:
I am happy to offer my help because we are close friends.

1. After the baseball game, they held a barbecue and gave out the awards.

   _____

   _____

2. Deep in the forest beneath the moonlight, the nocturnal animals scurried about.

   _____

   _____

3. Whenever she gave a speech in front of the class, she felt embarrassed and her face turned red.

   _____

   _____

4. If fitness is important to you, you should exercise regularly and eat proper food.

   _____

   _____

5. He didn't wake up in time because his alarm did not go off.

   _____

6. The students organized new teams before the tournament began.

   _____

ISBN: 978-1-897457-06-1

Creative Sentence Combinations

Example: The dog chased the cat. The cat climbed up a tree to escape. The tree was on the front lawn.

Might become:

When the dog chased the cat, it climbed up the tree on the front lawn to escape.

> *Some short sentences may be replaced by an adjective or adjective phrase.*

B. **Join the following short sentences to make one interesting sentence. It is not necessary to keep the sentences in the order that they appear.**

> *These transitional words and conjunctions help with combining sentences.*

whenever	although	after	before	during	while	if
because	where	when	even though	and	or	
but	even	even if	as	wherever	because of	

1. He delivered newspapers. He delivered newspapers every morning. He delivered newspapers even in bad weather.

   _____

   _____

2. The airport was crowded. There were many travellers. The travellers are on summer vacation.

   _____

   _____

3. He saved his money. He wanted to buy a new bicycle. He wanted an eighteen-speed bicycle.

   _____

   _____

4. The ice cream truck rang a bell. The children came running. They ran out of their houses.

   _____

   _____

Combining Sentences with Semicolons

A **semicolon** is often used to combine two closely related, short sentences.
A **conjunctive adverb** sometimes follows a semicolon to link firmly the two sentences.

Example: The car broke down; we were late for the appointment.

Might be written as:

The car broke down; consequently, we were late for the appointment.

C. **Combine the following short sentences and select an appropriate conjunctive adverb.**

Use each of these conjunctive adverbs once.

| consequently | unfortunately | otherwise | therefore |
| truly | however | nevertheless | sadly |

1. He had a good night's sleep. He was still tired.

   _____ ; _____ , _____ .

2. Lucy went to a summer camp. She was gone for two months.

   _____ ; _____ , _____ .

3. Paul arrived early for school. It was Saturday.

   _____ ; _____ , _____ .

4. The elderly lady needed help. There was no one around.

   _____ ; _____ , _____ .

5. She was chosen the top student. She received the award.

   _____ ; _____ , _____ .

6. Their team was the best. They wouldn't have won.

   _____ ; _____ , _____ .

7. The result was not as expected. They were happy.

   _____ ; _____ , _____ .

8. The cottage was enchanting. It was a special place.

   _____ ; _____ , _____ .

ISBN: 978-1-897457-06-1

Challenge

Below is a paragraph about the city of Toronto. This paragraph is made up of a series of short, choppy, and repetitive sentences. Convert each group into a single sentence and rewrite the passage.

The City of Toronto

(1) Toronto is a big city. Toronto is located in Ontario. Toronto is Canada's largest city. Toronto has a population of over 2 million people. (2) Toronto is located on a lake. The lake is Lake Ontario. Lake Ontario is one of the Great Lakes. There are five Great Lakes. (3) Toronto has many people. Many people are from foreign countries. Toronto is multicultural. Toronto is the most multicultural city in Canada. (4) Toronto is a banking centre. Toronto is a manufacturing centre. There are many job opportunities in Toronto. (5) Toronto is rated. The rating is in the top ten. The rating is about the best places to live and work in. The rating is about the best places in the world.

Be creative – change the word order to make concise, interesting sentences.

_____

_____

_____

_____

_____

_____

_____

_____

_____

6 Abstract and Concrete Language

Abstract language refers to words that represent ideas that do not have physical qualities. "Kindness" is an abstract word because it is a concept or idea. You cannot touch "kindness", but you can understand when someone is showing "kindness" by their actions.

A. State whether each of the following words is concrete or abstract. Place "A" for abstract and "C" for concrete in the space provided.

1. love ____   2. friend ____

3. responsibility ____   4. insect ____   5. flower ____

6. success ____   7. cloud ____   8. thoughts ____

9. laziness ____   10. happiness ____   11. fear ____

12. patio ____   13. freedom ____   14. democracy ____

15. photograph ____   16. automobile ____   17. oxygen ____

18. house ____   19. air ____   20. appetite ____

The Problem with Abstract Words

Abstract words are useful to express ideas but they do not always clarify what is being said.

Examples: 1. I feel good today.

   This sentence is somewhat vague. It might be written as:
   I feel well-rested today after a good night's sleep.

2. He was a responsible person.

   This sentence might become:
   Whenever he was given a job to do, he completed it on time.

          ISBN: 978-1-897457-06-1

B. **Interpret the meaning of each of these vague sentences. Then add details or descriptive words to make it more vivid.**

1. She had a nice time at the party.

   _____

   _____

2. He hurt his friend's feelings.

   _____

   _____

3. His father bought a new car.

   _____

   _____

4. Politeness goes a long way.

   _____

   _____

5. The results of the tests were good.

   _____

   _____

6. He worked hard to be successful.

   _____

   _____

7. He took time to collect his thoughts.

   _____

   _____

8. She finally achieved happiness after such a long time.

   _____

   _____

General and Specific Terms

Often we use words that are general and therefore do not give the reader a clear sense of what we are talking about. For example, we may refer to the furnishings in a room but the reader may not get a clear picture of the types of furniture or particular items of furniture.

C. For each general term below, list four specific items that may be part of that general group. The first one is done for you.

Furniture
1. *floral* loveseat
2. *antique dining* table
3. *leather* couch
4. *glass* coffee table

Think of various types of items under each classification. Use at least one adjective to describe each item.

Appliances
1. _____
2. _____
3. _____
4. _____

Food
1. _____
2. _____
3. _____
4. _____

Clothing
1. _____
2. _____
3. _____
4. _____

Animals
1. _____
2. _____
3. _____
4. _____

The Old House
1. _____
2. _____
3. _____
4. _____

The Seaside
1. _____
2. _____
3. _____
4. _____

ISBN: 978-1-897457-06-1

D. In each of the following sentences, there are vague, general terms that offer very little description. Replace the italicized words with more suitable words from the Word Bank below.

1. She entered the *space* and *sat down* in the seat.

   _____ _____

2. They had a *nice* time at the *gathering* held at the *restaurant*.

   _____ _____ _____

3. She was *keen* on trying *the sport*.

   _____ _____

4. Their cottage was *small* and it was *interesting*.

   _____ _____

5. The sky was *fine* and the wind was *good* – it was an *awesome* day for sailing.

   _____ _____ _____

6. She gave a *decent idea* to the *thing they argued about*.

   _____ _____ _____

7. The spotlight *lit up* the stadium; the *people made noise*.

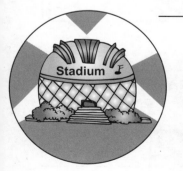

   _____ _____ _____

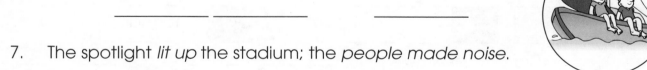

Word Bank			
intelligent	slumped	fans	quaint
anxious	enjoyable	response	ideal
banquet hall	clear	family room	
cozy	debate	cheered	
illuminated	water skiing	balmy	
birthday party			

ISBN: 978-1-897457-06-1

7 Building Vocabulary (1)

A. Build derivative words from the lead words given. Match the derivative word with the word description requested.

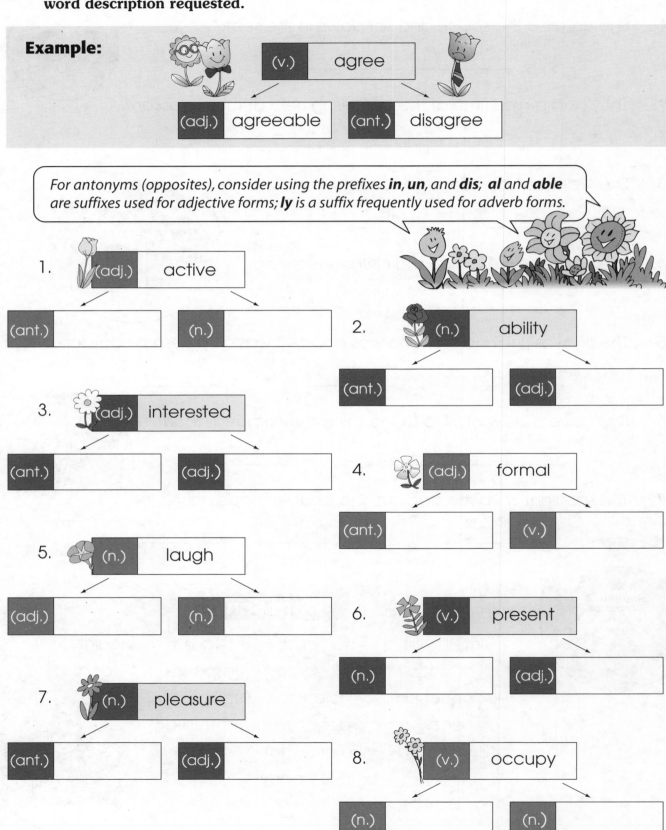

Example:

(v.) agree

(adj.) agreeable   (ant.) disagree

*For antonyms (opposites), consider using the prefixes **in**, **un**, and **dis**; **al** and **able** are suffixes used for adjective forms; **ly** is a suffix frequently used for adverb forms.*

1. (adj.) active

(ant.)   (n.)

2. (n.) ability

(ant.)   (adj.)

3. (adj.) interested

(ant.)   (adj.)

4. (adj.) formal

(ant.)   (v.)

5. (n.) laugh

(adj.)   (n.)

6. (v.) present

(n.)   (adj.)

7. (n.) pleasure

(ant.)   (adj.)

8. (v.) occupy

(n.)   (n.)

Root Words

The root word is the basic word from which other words are derived.

Example: Root word "happy"

Derivatives: unhappy, happily, happiness

B. **Identify the root word for each of the following words.**

1. problematic _____

2. annoyance _____

3. disregard _____

4. creation _____

5. disturbance _____

6. disinterested _____

7. incredible _____

8. royalty _____

9. truthfulness _____

10. colonize _____

11. extinction _____

12. mischievous _____

13. hopeless _____

14. reduction _____

15. sensory _____

16. delicacy _____

17. regrettable _____

18. wholesomeness _____

19. disenchantment _____

20. representation _____

Prefixes

These are common prefixes for forming new words:

hyper – more than usual or expected; more
hypo – less than usual or expected; under, less
mis – wrong or bad
extra – at a level beyond; outside the range of
pre – before; at a previous time
retro – backwards; back in time
pro – in favour of; for
out – better than, greater than; separate from

C. Write a brief meaning or a synonym for each of the words below. Use each word in a sentence to show its meaning.

1. extraordinary : _____
   Sentence : _____

2. hyperactive : _____
   Sentence : _____

3. misdirected : _____
   Sentence : _____

4. retrospect : _____
   Sentence : _____

5. promotion : _____
   Sentence : _____

6. hypersensitive : _____
   Sentence : _____

7. outrageous : _____
   Sentence : _____

8. extracurricular : _____
   Sentence : _____

9. outdo : _____
   Sentence : _____

10. protector : _____
    Sentence : _____

ISBN: 978-1-897457-06-1

Word Sleuth – Discovering New Words from Context

Context refers to the sentence in which a word is used that helps define its meaning.

Example: To climb the mountain presented an extraordinary challenge.
(Without necessarily knowing the meaning of the word "extraordinary", the sense of the sentence tells you that it means something great or out of the scope of what is expected.)

D. **Read each sentence below. Then circle the definition that best suits the meaning of the italicized word in the sentence.**

1. The *painstaking* work in the hot sun was rewarded with a huge payment.

   easy   casual   difficult   routine

2. He had only a *superficial* understanding of the problem and was therefore unable to solve it.

   deep   shallow   detailed   thorough

3. He used his *ingenuity* to figure out the mathematical problem.

   stupidity   intelligence   laziness   thoughts

4. Because of the *inflammatory* remark made about him, he demanded an apology.

   complimentary   pleasant   insulting   correct

5. Wayne Gretzky was the most *prolific* scorer in the history of hockey.

   occasional   regular   abundant   infrequent

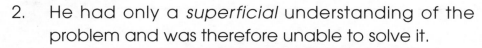

6. She was *perturbed* by the noise of the crowd so she went home.

   annoyed   overjoyed   happy   excited

7. She reached the *zenith* of her tennis career when she won the Wimbledon title.

   bottom   end   height   level

8. The *ubiquitous* clouds completely covered the sky before the rainfall.

   small   all-present   fluffy   white

PROGRESS TEST 1

A. Match each of the following words with its meaning.

1. unimportant _____   A. anticipation
2. surprised _____   B. scurried
3. strange _____   C. trivia
4. eagerness _____   D. brush
5. bushes _____   E. shocked
6. scampered _____   F. eerie

B. Match each of the descriptive words below with its definition.

1. treacherous _____   A. a type of race

2. quaint _____   B. dangerous

3. graceful _____   C. tired

4. exciting _____   D. rang

5. soared _____   E. with fine movement

6. experienced _____   F. tasty

7. delicious _____   G. fought against

8. struggled _____   H. crushed, broke

9. chimed _____   I. thrilling

10. smashed _____   J. streaked through the air

11. marathon _____   K. felt, knew, went through

12. exhausted _____   L. cute, old-fashioned

 Complete EnglishSmart • **Grade 6**   ISBN: 978-1-897457-06-1

C. **Select the correct word to suit the context of each sentence below.**

1. He was _____ (too, to, two) tired to walk the _____ (too, to, two) kilometres _____ (too, to, two) the store.

2. She would rather play (than, then) _____ work.

3. The newscaster said that the _____ (weather, whether) was going to be cold and rainy.

4. _____ (Weather, Whether) or not they decide to play depends on how much time they have.

5. _____ (Its, It's) always interesting to visit the museum.

6. Her dog was hungry so she put _____ (its, it's) food in the dish.

7. _____ (There, Their, They're) neighbour asked for help cutting the lawn.

8. She asked when _____ (there, their, they're) going shopping.

9. He sat over _____ (there, their, they're) near the middle of the room.

10. She _____ (threw, through) a birthday party for her friend.

11. He _____ (threw, through) the ball _____ (threw, through) the window.

12. He tripped because his shoelace was _____ (loose, lose).

13. If they don't play well, they'll _____ (loose, lose) the game.

14. _____ (Whose, Who's) at the door?

15. _____ (Whose, Who's) boots are these at the front door?

16. He _____ (quiet, quite, quit) the school team.

17. Be _____ (quiet, quite, quit) in a hospital zone.

18. He was _____ (quiet, quite, quit) sure he wasn't to blame.

19. He was told to _____ (wait, weight) in front of the school.

20. Because he was thin, he was worried about his _____ (wait, weight).

D. **Some words are unnecessary in the following sentences. Write these sentences after removing the unnecessary words.**

1. In my opinion, I think that exercise is important.

_____

2. My friend who is very tall is an excellent student.

_____

3. I think it was in my view an important day for him.

_____

4. I'm not sure and I might be wrong, I remember that he dropped by last Tuesday.

_____

5. What I don't quite understand is how they could walk away from the terrible accident unhurt.

_____

6. It was in fact a great day for flying kites.

_____

ISBN: 978-1-897457-06-1

Make one sentence out of the following groups of sentences.

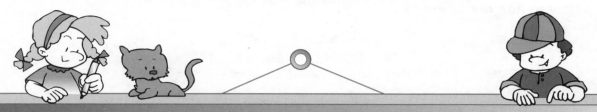

1. The rain poured down. We got soaked.

   _____

2. We laughed at the comedian. He was very funny.

   _____

3. The lights went out. We were frightened.

   _____

4. We had a garage sale. We sold lots of things. We made some money.

   _____

5. The bus broke down. We waited for another bus. We waited a long time.

   _____

6. The game was tied. The game went into overtime. There was no winner.

   _____

7. I received a video game from my best friend, Jason, for my birthday. I couldn't be happier. We played it right away.

   _____

   _____

8. The meeting was lengthy. It dragged on and on for almost five hours. Everybody was bored except the Chairman.

   _____

   _____

F. **Use a semicolon to combine the following sentences. Add one of the conjunctive adverbs below to link the sentences.**

however   therefore   otherwise   sadly   luckily

1. It was a rainy day. The baseball game was cancelled.

   It was a rainy day; _____ , _____

2. I awoke in the middle of the night. I was able to get back to sleep shortly afterwards.

   _____

   _____

3. We didn't play well. Our captain scored the decisive goal just before the end of the game.

   _____

   _____

4. The results were posted. We did not win.

   _____

5. Their project was the best. They wouldn't have won the prize.

   _____

G. **Identify each word below as either concrete or abstract by placing the letter "C" for concrete or "A" for abstract in the space provided.**

1. love _____   Concrete   2. freedom _____   Abstract

3. president _____   4. maple _____

5. fear _____   6. patio _____

7. lily _____   8. pain _____

9. idea _____   10. friendship _____

H. Write the root word of each of the following words.

1. problematic _____ 2. colonize _____

3. reduction _____ 4. delicacy _____

5. representation _____ 6. annoyance _____

7. considerate _____ 8. disillusioned _____

9. extraordinarily _____ 10. unemotional _____

I. Create two new words for each of the following root words. Use an antonym and a synonym where possible.

1. agree   a. _____ b. _____
2. interest   a. _____ b. _____
3. present   a. _____ b. _____
4. laugh   a. _____ b. _____
5. occupy   a. _____ b. _____
6. disturb   a. _____ b. _____
7. please   a. _____ b. _____
8. doubt   a. _____ b. _____
9. decide   a. _____ b. _____
10. place   a. _____ b. _____

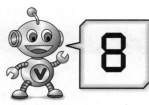

8 Building Vocabulary (2)

Homonym Challenge

Homonyms are words that sound the same but have different meanings. They are easily confused.

Examples: (a) an insect – a bee
(b) to exist – be

A. Take the "homonym challenge". For each pair of homonyms, there are two clues. Write the homonyms.

1. (a) finished eating : _____ (b) a number : _____

2. (a) day of the week : _____ (b) ice cream treat : _____

3. (a) to reduce : _____ (b) something learned : _____

4. (a) forest animal : _____ (b) without clothing : _____

5. (a) run away from : _____ (b) treat after dinner : _____

6. (a) head of the school : _____ (b) key point or idea : _____

7. (a) dogs' feet : _____ (b) break in the action : _____

8. (a) a coin : _____ (b) an odour : _____

9. (a) people in the hospital : _____

   (b) needed when waiting : _____

10. (a) a type of blue pants : _____

    (b) biological molecules : _____

ISBN: 978-1-897457-06-1

Antonym Challenge

An antonym is a word that is opposite in meaning to another word.

Examples: good / bad   smooth / rough   wet / dry

B. In the "antonym challenge", some letters of the antonym of each word are given; there is an additional clue in parentheses. Find the word that fits.

1.	enlarge	r e __ u c __	(make smaller)
2.	seldom	a __ w __ __ s	(every time)
3.	remember	__ o r __ __ t	(put out of mind)
4.	slow	__ u __ c __	(very fast)
5.	outside	__ __ s __ __ e	(sheltered)
6.	initial	f __ n __ __	(the last one)
7.	loss	p __ __ f __ t	(the amount gained)
8.	occupied	v __ __ a __ t	(like an empty house)
9.	clear	v a __ __ e	(a little hard to understand)
10.	stupid	__ l e __ e r	(quick thinker)
11.	bulky	c __ m p __ c t	(handy)
12.	quiet	n __ i __ y	(very loud)

Synonym Challenge

A synonym is a word that means the same as another word.

Examples: high / lofty   fast / quick   old / ancient

C. In the "synonym challenge", some letters of the synonym of each word are given; there is an additional clue in parentheses. Find the word that fits.

1.	blow up	i n f __ __ t __	(like a tire)
2.	run	o __ e __ a __ e	(like a machine)
3.	inhabitant	n __ t i __ e	(could be born there)
4.	delight	p l __ __ s __	(make someone happy)
5.	defend	p __ o t __ __ t	(act as a guardian)
6.	talk	c __ __ t	(casual conversation)
7.	examine	a n a __ __ z __	(look at closely)
8.	compute	c o __ __ t	(as with numbers)
9.	magic	w __ z __ __ d __ y	(like Harry Potter)
10.	prediction	p r __ g __ o s __ s	(a doctor's prediction)
11.	example	s __ e c __ m __ n	(might be found in a lab)
12.	vacate	a __ a __ d __ n	(to leave suddenly)

Fast = Quick

ISBN: 978-1-897457-06-1

D. Place a synonym or a short definition of each italicized word in the space provided.

The italicized words in the sentences below may not be familiar to you. However, once you read the sentences, their meanings should be clear.

1. The *precise* directions were *beneficial* in helping them find their way.

   _____   _____

2. The *mammoth* elephant *towered* over the other animals in the zoo.

   _____   _____

3. The doctor's *prognosis* was that he would *recover* fully in about three weeks.

   _____   _____

4. Because she was such a *virtuous* person, she could not tell a lie.

   _____

5. The *docile* cat *slumbered* in the warm sunshine.

   _____   _____

6. She *analyzed* the *specimen* to determine its *classification*.

   _____   _____   _____

7. She *reflected* on the *peculiar* situation before making a decision.

   _____   _____

8. The huge red balloon was *conspicuous* to everyone including those far away.

   _____

9. He was an *ardent* fan of the Toronto Blue Jays and attended every home game.

   _____

10. The *agile* player made a quick *manoeuvre* to avoid the defence.

    _____   _____

9 Writing Poetry

Rhyming Word Challenge

A. Write three rhyming words for each lead word.

1. chrome	2. clog	3. day	4. pipe

_____ _____ _____ _____

_____ _____ _____ _____

_____ _____ _____ _____

5. hint	6. hop	7. super	8. bring

_____ _____ _____ _____

_____ _____ _____ _____

_____ _____ _____ _____

9. blink	10. food	11. rock	12. job

_____ _____ _____ _____

_____ _____ _____ _____

_____ _____ _____ _____

13. ducks	14. cow	15. rude	16. diner

_____ _____ _____ _____

_____ _____ _____ _____

_____ _____ _____ _____

ISBN: 978-1-897457-06-1

Acrostic Poems

An acrostic poem is a poem in which the first letters of the lines form a word or words.

Example: **JANICE SMITH**

Jumps skipping rope
Always visits her grandmother
Never tells a lie
Invents games to play
Cares about people
Energy to burn

Spends a lot of time at home
Memorizes a poem
Interested in who you are
Takes trips very far
Happy when riding in the car

In the example above, the first name lines don't rhyme but the lines of the last name do.

B.   Write an acrostic poem with your full name. Where possible try and create rhyming lines.

AN ACROSTIC POEM

_____   _____

_____   _____

_____   _____

_____   _____

_____   _____

_____   _____

_____   _____

_____   _____

_____   _____

_____   _____

_____   _____

_____   _____

ISBN: 978-1-897457-06-1

9

Opposites

Read these two 2-line poems that speak about opposites. The last words of the lines rhyme.

1. The opposite of fun
   Is going to bed when the day is done
2. What is the opposite of eating a big lunch
   Enjoying grapes in a bunch

C. **Here are some first lines for you. Add a second line to complete the opposite idea.**

1. Rather than sit feeling sad

   _____

2. It's better to be tucked in bed

   _____

3. Having a good book to read

   _____

4. My dog doesn't like to play

   _____

5. It's too hard to catch a frog

   _____

6. The opposite of an empty room

   _____

7. The opposite of being afraid

   _____

8. The opposite of feeling blue

   _____

ISBN: 978-1-897457-06-1

Synonym Poems

A synonym poem contains:

1. a title which is the lead word / idea for the synonym group.
2. a rhyming couplet – two lines that rhyme.
3. a first line that contains three or more synonym words.

Example:

Cake
Delicious, scrumptious, mouth-watering, and tasty
We devoured the cake till our plates were empty.

D. **For each title below, create a synonym poem. Use a thesaurus if you need help, and make the last word in your synonym list one that's easy to rhyme.**

1. FRUITS

_____

_____

2. FRIENDS

_____

_____

3. FAMILY VACATION

_____

_____

4. CAMPING GEAR

_____

_____

5. RELATIVES

_____

_____

ISBN: 978-1-897457-06-1

10 Imagery in Poetry

When you write a poem, you are creating images that make readers use their imagination.

Examples:

WORD	PRECISE WORD (synonym)	IMAGE
bird	canary	the colour yellow
food	oranges	the tangy taste and orange colour
car	red Miata	a convertible sports car
house	cottage	quaint dwelling in the country

Each example above shows how a more precise word (synonym) from a word category creates a sharper image for the reader.

A. Use a more precise word in place of each of the following words to create a sharper image.

1. child ⟹ _____

2. fish ⟹ _____

3. flower ⟹ _____

4. animal ⟹ _____

5. athlete ⟹ _____

6. award ⟹ _____

7. book ⟹ _____

8. sweater ⟹ _____

9. coat ⟹ _____

10. said ⟹ _____

11. went ⟹ _____

12. hit ⟹ _____

13. looked ⟹ _____

14. happy ⟹ _____

15. toy ⟹ _____

16. pet ⟹ _____

ISBN: 978-1-897457-06-1

Working with Similes

A simile is a comparison of two things using "like" or "as".

Examples: She ran as swift **as a deer**.
Like a soaring eagle, the kite climbed the sky.

B. Finish each description below with a simile. You can use a single word or phrase. Add articles (a, an, the) as needed.

1. eyes as black as _____
2. quick like _____
3. a smile like _____
4. sneaky as _____
5. funny as _____
6. happy as _____
7. hair like _____
8. bright as _____

Metaphors

A metaphor is an implied comparison. That is, two unlike things are compared for the purpose of creating a common idea.

Examples: Life is **an ever-flowing river**.
The hands of time wait for no one.

A metaphor is similar to a simile without the use of "like" or "as".

C. Create metaphors for the following items.

1. Her life is a (an) _____ .

2. The sun, a _____ , shone brightly over the land.

3. The runner, a _____ , limped along.

4. Her eyes, two _____ , stared straight ahead.

5. His smile is a _____ that warms the heart.

6. The raindrops, _____ , showered the flowers.

10

Personification

Personification is a figurative language device that gives human qualities to inanimate objects.

Example:

The sun **smiled** upon the flowers.

(In this example the sun didn't actually **smile**. The implication is that the light from the sun warmed the flowers.)

D.   Fill in the blanks with verbs that personify the inanimate subjects.

1.   The birds _____ a song of freedom.

2.   The sea _____ up to the shore line.

3.   The weeping willow _____ alongside the river.

4.   The old maple tree _____ its branches to the sky.

5.   The old house _____ its first inhabitants.

6.   The flowers _____ in the wind.

7.   The dog _____ its master.

8.   The boats _____ along the dock.

9.   The old reliable car _____ along the highway.

10.   The hyena _____ at the other jungle animals.

11.   Her thoughts _____ around in her head.

12.   The hurricane _____ the village houses.

ISBN: 978-1-897457-06-1

E. Complete each line using similes, metaphors, or personification as you see fit to create description. It is not necessary to make the verses rhyme.

1

The Sea

The white-capped waves _____

The sea gulls _____

The wind and surf _____

The sailboats _____

2

The Playground

The merry-go-round _____

The swings _____

The children on the slide _____

Happy faces _____

3

The Storm

Dark clouds _____

Thunder and lightning _____

The moon _____

Rain _____

11 Word Origins

Many words in the English language originated from Greek or Latin words, suffixes and prefixes. In fact the word "suffix" comes from the Latin word "fix" which means "to fasten".

Examples: astr (star) – astronomy, astrology

A. For each Latin and Greek origin, create a common English word.

GREEK DERIVATIVES

1. metr (measure) _____
2. geo (earth) _____
3. graph (writing) _____
4. tele (far off) _____
5. path (feeling) _____
6. phys (nature) _____
7. bio (life) _____
8. phil (love) _____

LATIN DERIVATIVES

9. audi (to hear) _____
10. manu (hand) _____
11. op (work) _____
12. scrib (write) _____
13. jur (law) _____
14. vid (see) _____
15. bene (good) _____
16. dict (speak) _____

B. Think of a word to suit each definition.

In some cases the prefix is given; in other cases the root word is given.

1. half the earth .... hemi _____

2. a single train track ...... mono _____

3. a hundred years .... cent _____

ISBN: 978-1-897457-06-1

4.   thousand metres.......... _____ metre

5.   say the opposite .... con _____

6.   opposite of arrive .... _____ part

7.   lower its worth .... de _____

8.   fail to comprehend ..... _____ understand

9.   predict the weather .... fore _____

10. after the battle .... post _____

Noun Suffixes

Here are some typical suffixes that, when attached to a root word, form nouns:
ance, hood, ness, dom, ship, tion, sion, ence, or, er

C.   **Use each of the above suffixes only once to form a new word. In cases where the suffix is provided, use the definition to create the word.**

1.   the royal territory .... king _____

2.   to have something .... owner _____

3.   one who performs .... _____ er

4.   the opposition .... competi _____

5.   a feeling of joy .... _____ ness

6.   being a father .... father _____

7.   differ between .... _____ ence

8.   sympathy .... compas _____

9.   one who plays against .... competit _____

10. a chance happening ..... circumst _____

11

D. Create words using the following verb suffixes: ize, ate, ify, en. In cases where the suffix is provided, use the definition to create the word.

1. to use…util _____

2. to prove true…ver _____

3. to make a deal…negoti _____

4. to hurry up…hast _____

5. feel sorrow…sy _____ ize

6. to make or build…c _____ ate

7. to make simple…si _____ ify

8. to untie…lo _____ en

E. Use the following suffixes to form adjectives: ful, able, al, tic, ish, tive, less, ious.

> *Use each suffix only once to form a new word. In cases where the suffix is provided, use the definition to create the word.*

1. hard to believe…fantas _____

2. without purpose…u _____ less

3. only a part of…p _____ al

4. tastes great…scrumpt _____

5. full of energy…a _____ tive

6. dependable…re _____ able

7. easily embarrassed…bash _____

8. very trendy…styl _____

ISBN: 978-1-897457-06-1

Word Sleuth Challenge

F. Match each word with its meaning. Place the letter of the definition beside the word it defines. Refer to the list of Greek and Latin roots given earlier in this unit. The prefixes are underlined for you.

You may not be familiar with these words. However, if you look closely at the root of each word, you should be able to match it with the synonym or definition given.

1.	<u>au</u>dible	A.	large hall or theatre
2.	<u>ben</u>ign	B.	create a picture in your mind
3.	<u>fore</u>shadow	C.	person who does good for another
4.	<u>super</u>b	D.	visually splendid scenery
5.	<u>post</u>pone	E.	safe, good, kind
6.	<u>astro</u>logy	F.	scribbling, writing on walls
7.	<u>gra</u>ffiti	G.	pitiful
8.	<u>co</u>operative	H.	engraving, writing
9.	<u>bene</u>factor	I.	predict the future, look ahead
10.	<u>dict</u>ator	J.	can be heard
11.	<u>vis</u>ualize	K.	wonderful, great, excellent
12.	<u>just</u>ify	L.	put to a later date
13.	<u>in</u>scription	M.	horoscope, study of stars and planets
14.	<u>pa</u>thetic	N.	helpful, working well with others
15.	<u>vis</u>ta	O.	make excuse for, give reason for
16.	<u>audi</u>torium	P.	tyrant, controller in government

12 Writing Ads and Announcements

Cottage for Rent

Lakefront cottage. Sleeps six. Boat, beach, safe swimming. Ideal for children. $2\frac{1}{2}$ hours from city. $800/week.

Expanded Version

This quaint cottage rental is located on a quiet lake just two and a half hours north of the city. This spacious cottage sleeps up to six people and is ideal for children with its safe swimming and sandy beach. A motor boat is included in the rental rate of $800.00 per week.

A. **For each of the more detailed advertisements below, write a brief advertisement that covers the main points in the fewest words.**

Leave out any unnecessary or obvious details.

1.

Bike for Sale

A youth's 18-speed, 42-cm-frame mountain bike, red with white racing stripes, is offered for sale for $125.00. It has new tires, excellent gears, and a comfortable seat. It includes a carrier, reflectors, and a kickstand. This bike is like new and has been in storage for nearly a year.

Ad Version

_____

_____

_____

2.

House for Rent

Located close to shopping malls, schools, and transportation, this three-bedroom detached back-split house is an ideal family home. There is a large, private garden and an attached garage. The basement is finished with a playroom and a second washroom. This house is available on October 1st at a rental rate of $1,400.00 per month.

ISBN: 978-1-897457-06-1

_____

_____

_____

3.

Want Ad – Employment – Delivery Boy / Girl

A busy neighbourhood pharmacy is looking for a reliable, mature, responsible youth to assume delivery responsibilities in the neighbourhood after school and on weekends. This individual must be outgoing and friendly, and enjoy meeting people. Punctuality and dedication is expected. A bicycle is provided and an hourly rate of $7.25 is offered.

Ad Version

_____

_____

_____

B. Expand the following ad to be more detailed and descriptive.

Expanded Version

_____

_____

_____

_____

_____

_____

_____

_____

_____

_____

GARAGE SALE

Garage sale. Sunday, October 11, 9 – 3. Appliances, furniture, clothing, toys, electronics, sports equipment, antiques, etc. Everything must go.

ISBN: 978-1-897457-06-1

12

C. **Create interesting and exciting ads for the following. Include enough details to answer all basic questions that the reader of the ad may have.**

1

Help Wanted – Babysitter

_____
_____
_____
_____

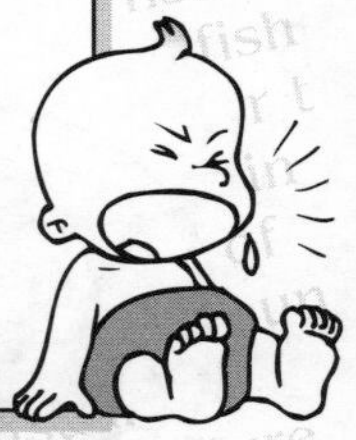

2

Toys and Games for Sale

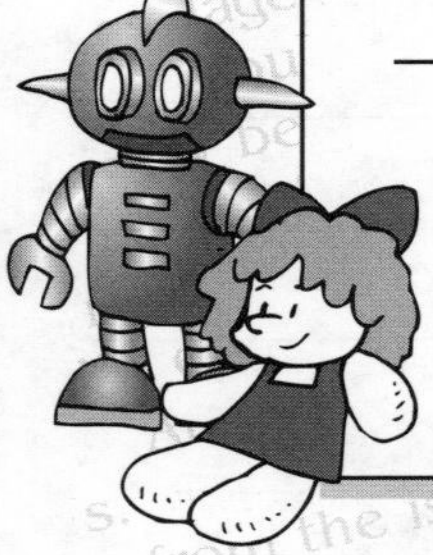

_____
_____
_____

3

Student Available for Yard Cleanup and Odd Jobs

_____
_____
_____
_____

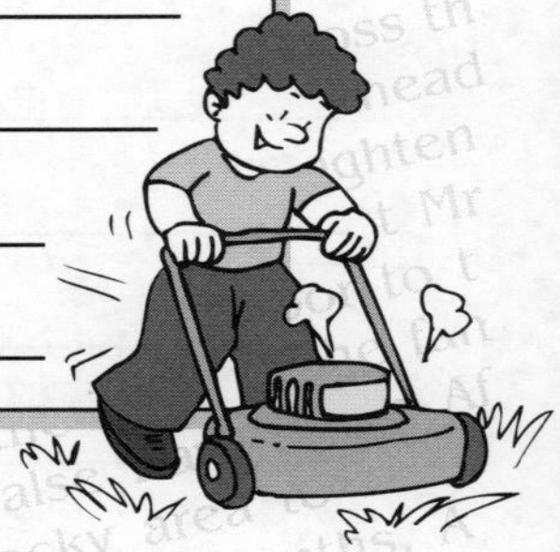

4

Fundraising Car Wash on Saturday

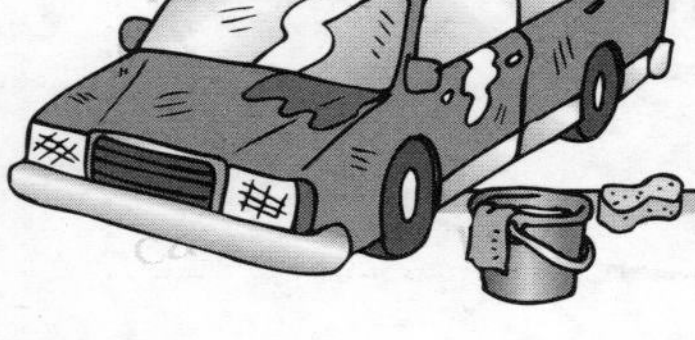

_____
_____
_____

Writing Announcements

An announcement is a brief, direct piece of information. Its intention is to inform people of an event while anticipating a reader's basic questions.

Which is the better announcement? Why is it better?

It's Susan's birthday and you're invited!

Date : Saturday, July 15
Time : 1:30 pm – 6:00 pm
Location : 126 Spruce Ave.

(Rides will be provided if necessary.)
Confirm by Monday, July 10.
Call 444-222-3333.

Birthday Party

You are invited to a birthday party for Susan on Saturday. Please confirm by Monday. If you need a ride, contact Susan's mother, Mrs. Johnston.

D. Compose announcements for the following events.

1.   Cat Missing

_____
_____
_____
_____
                _____
                _____

2.   School Play

_____
_____
_____
_____
_____

3.   Funfair

_____
_____
_____
                _____
                _____
                _____

4.   Speech Contest

_____
_____
_____
_____
_____

13 Letter Writing

The Friendly Letter

The friendly letter is an informal, casual way of communicating with friends and family.

Example

two-paragraph structure

Hi Paula, ⬅ **informal salutation**

How are you? Hope all is well with you and your family. I will be up north near your cottage and would like to pop in for a visit.

Call me or drop me an email and we can arrange to get together.

Your buddy, ⬅ **casual closing**

Joanna

A. Write a friendly letter to your friend who is now settling in another place. Tell him/her something great that happened to you.

_____ ,

_____

_____

_____

_____

_____

_____

_____ ,

_____

Informal Writing

Informal writing does not always follow precise rules of grammar. The sentence structure is often quite casual. People write informally in emails, notes, friendly letters, invitations, thank you notes, or on greeting cards. Informal writing with brief sentences or utterances is particularly useful when space is limited.

Example

Informal

Hi Lucy...how are you?

Just arrived in beautiful Paris. Awesome. Got our hotel, had lunch by the Seine. Going to see the Mona Lisa tomorrow. Hope all is well. Take care.

Janet

Formal

Dear Lucy,

I finally have arrived in Paris and I can't begin to describe how beautiful the city is. We checked into our hotel and had lunch at a café alongside River Seine. Tomorrow we will go to the Louvre to view the Mona Lisa. I will write again soon. I hope all is well with you at home.

Sincerely,
Janet

Note the difference in the structure of the sentences.

B. **Assume you are on holiday at a far off place, perhaps a place you've dreamt of visiting. Compose a postcard to a friend or family member giving as many details as possible in a small space.**

13

The Formal Letter

A formal or business letter has a specific purpose and is usually written in a three-paragraph format.

Paragraph 1 – states the purpose of your letter
Paragraph 2 – gives details about the subject of your letter
Paragraph 3 – suggests a course of action; offers a solution; asks for follow-up contact

Below is a sample letter of request to a retail supplier.

formal salutation, followed by a colon

Dear Mr. Anderson:

first paragraph states purpose

I am writing to request a refund for the computer game "Outer Limits" that I recently purchased from Future World Depot. Enclosed please find a copy of my receipt and the complete package that was purchased.

second paragraph gives details of the problem

I had difficulty downloading the programme and each time I went through the process, the programme cancelled itself. I am able to load up many other programmes so I do not think there is a problem with my computer.

third paragraph offers suggestion

Kindly forward a refund in the full amount of the invoice enclosed. Thank you for your attention in this matter.

formal closing

Sincerely,

LAURA MARCOS

ISBN: 978-1-897457-06-1

C. Write a formal letter to a company telling them how much you enjoyed their product.

_____ :

_____

_____

_____

_____

_____

_____

_____

_____

_____

_____ ,

_____

14 Interviewing Celebrities

Shania Twain was born in Windsor, Ontario in 1965. She has become one of the world's leading country / pop singers, having sold millions of albums worldwide. She currently resides in Switzerland.

Shania Twain

Avril Lavigne was born in Napanee, Ontario in 1984. At the age of 14, she began her recording career. Her debut album, "Let Go", was released in 2002 and has sold over 16,000,000 copies to date.

Avril Lavigne

Jim Carrey was born in Newmarket, Ontario on January 17, 1962. Carrey is recognized as one of the funniest comedic actors in the business today. His numerous films including "Cable Guy", "The Mask", and "Dumb and Dumber" have made him famous and popular with all age groups.

Jim Carrey

Bill Gates

Bill Gates, born in 1955, is the founder of Microsoft Corporation. He is responsible for developing software programmes that run virtually all the world's computers. Gates is the wealthiest man in the world with a net worth estimated at close to 58 billion US dollars.

Born in Austria in 1947, Arnold Schwarzenegger became interested in body-building at an early age. By the age of 23, he had won the Mr. Universe contest. He went on to become an actor and is now best known for his lead role in the "Terminator" film series. He is now the Governor of California.

Arnold Schwarzenegger

Complete EnglishSmart • **Grade 6** ISBN: 978-1-897457-06-1

Weak Questions and Detailed Questions

Weak Question: Do you like pizza?

(A simple yes or no response would suffice here.)

**Detailed Question: What was the biggest difficulty that you had
to overcome in your rise to stardom?**

(This question encourages the celebrity to go into detail.)

A. Pretend that you are an interviewer for a well-known magazine. Choose two of the celebrities on the adjacent page to interview. Your task is to create interesting questions to get the most detailed answers out of them.

Celebrity 1:

Questions:

1. _____
2. _____
3. _____
4. _____
5. _____

Celebrity 2:

Questions:

1. _____
2. _____
3. _____
4. _____
5. _____

14

Tricky Usage

B. The following are examples of tricky usage choices that frequently cause confusion. Read the explanations and complete the sentences with the correct choices.

1. "less" and "fewer": use **less** when referring to quantity; use **fewer** when referring to units

He drank _____ pop.

He drank _____ cans of pop.

2. "lie" and "lay": **lie** means <u>to rest</u> in a certain position; **lay** means <u>to place</u> something

She _____ the book on the table and walked away.

She _____ down on the couch when she's tired.

3. "sit" and "set": **sit** means to take a seat; **set** means to place something somewhere

She _____ in her own seat.

He _____ the table for dinner.

 ISBN: 978-1-897457-06-1

4. "in" and "into": **in** means <u>inside</u>; **into** refers to the <u>movement</u> from outside to inside

She lived _____ the neighbourhood.

He moved _____ a new apartment.

5. "may" and "can": **may** concerns <u>permission</u>; **can** refers to <u>ability</u>

_____ we go to the movies?

_____ you ride a bike?

6. "lend" and "borrow": **lend** refers to <u>giving</u> something out on loan; **borrow** refers to <u>receiving</u> something on loan

May I _____ your pen?

She will _____ her pen to her friend.

7. "among" and "between": **among** is used when referring to a group of <u>more than two</u>; **between** is used when referring to <u>two people or things</u>

She couldn't decide _____ the red or the blue dress.

Who _____ the orchestra have practised their notes?

15 Preparing to Run a Marathon

Running a marathon is the <u>ultimate</u> test of physical fitness. It's true that most people know how to run, and that most can run across the street to catch a bus or run over to a neighbour's house with little difficulty. Running a marathon, however, is quite a different challenge.

The first step for many will be to purchase an expensive pair of running shoes. This may be a good idea but it is far from the most important first step in the training process. The official distance of a marathon run is 26 miles 385 feet (42 kilometres). In order to complete this distance, a runner, and certainly a <u>novice</u> runner, must prepare carefully. First, a person should get a physical check-up from his or her doctor to ensure that running such a long distance is safe. Once this is <u>confirmed</u>, the training can begin. For a person who is a beginning runner, it takes a <u>minimum</u> of three months or, in most cases, much longer to properly train for a marathon. In addition to long hours of training, it is important that the runner avoids illness and injury.

Novice runners should begin with <u>brisk</u>, lengthy walks. Running can begin after a few weeks of regular walking sessions with increased speed and distance at consistent intervals. Training should involve running at least five days a week with a steady distance increase of 15 – 20% every two weeks. As training intensifies, longer runs should become part of the training. For example, it is suggested that a long run of 24 to 30 kilometres should become a regular part of training once the runner is getting close to the race day. It is also recommended that, to <u>offset</u> the longer training run, a short run (5 to 8 kilometres) one day a week be part of the <u>routine</u> including one day of complete rest.

The marathon run is a <u>gruelling</u>, <u>exhausting</u> test of strength, <u>stamina</u>, and aerobic fitness. Anyone who completes the race, regardless of his or her overall final race standing, can be proud of having <u>accomplished</u> one of the most difficult tests of physical endurance.

ISBN: 978-1-897457-06-1

A. Complete the crossword puzzle with the words found in the passage.

Across

A. programme
B. energy
C. greatest, extreme
D. quick
E. new, inexperienced

Down

1. demanding, difficult
2. proved to be true
3. balance out
4. tiring
5. at least
6. completed

MARATHON

FINISH

15

Expository Writing

The purpose of an expository composition is to explain, to inform, and in some cases, to persuade.

Example: Preparing to Run a Marathon

Paragraph 1 – introduction to topic Paragraph 2 – step one: preparing to train

Paragraph 3 – step two: training steps Paragraph 4 – conclusion

B. Choose one of the following topics and write an expository composition following a similar structure to the one in "Preparing to Run a Marathon".

Learning to Ride a Bike   Making Scrambled Eggs

Organizing a Funfair   Organizing a Car Wash

Preparing for a Garage Sale   The Tricks of Being a Goalkeeper

Title: _____

Introduction: State and explain details of your topic or make a statement to create interest in your topic.

_____

_____

Paragraph Two: "How to" steps to follow

_____

_____

_____

_____

_____

_____

Conclusion: Make a summary statement or add a final related idea.

_____

_____

_____

Editorial Writing

An editorial is an opinion piece found in a newspaper or magazine. Some editorials are quite lengthy especially when the topic is detailed and complex. Other editorials are quite brief and state a simple, straightforward opinion. A short editorial is often personal in tone and written in the first person "I".

Editorial

MONDAY, SEPTEMBER 15, 2004

Are drivers in the city getting worse or is it just my imagination?

As a regular bike rider, I am constantly in fear of my life as reckless city drivers disobey the basic rules. The other day, I encountered, on four separate occasions, drivers who failed to stop at stop signs in residential areas. These drivers know that their chances of getting caught in a quiet neighbourhood are slim and so they take advantage by behaving in a criminally negligent manner. I am sick of being run off the road by these maniacs and demand that the police devise a method of catching them in the act. Perhaps a loss of licence for a month for one of these infractions would impress upon them the importance of road safety.

C. **Do the following based on the above piece of editorial writing.**

1. Compose a different opening sentence.

   _____

   _____

2. Compose a different concluding sentence.

   _____

   _____

3. Create one other example of danger or one other incident to prove your point.

   _____

   _____

   _____

   _____

A. Give a homonym for each of the following words.

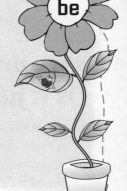

1. bee _____
2. jeans _____
3. scent _____
4. eight _____
5. week _____
6. sundae _____
7. bear _____
8. lessen _____
9. guessed _____
10. dessert _____
11. principal _____
12. patience _____
13. idol _____
14. pause _____

B. Solve the antonym puzzles by filling in the missing letters.

1. reduce   e __ l a r __ __ __
2. always   s __ l d __ m
3. forget   r e __ e m __ e r
4. quiet   v o c __ f e __ o u s
5. hide   __ e __ e __ l
6. clever   __ __ u __ i __
7. profit   l __ s __
8. vacant   o c c __ __ i e d
9. vague   c l __ __ r
10. final   i n i __ i a __
11. surface   c __ r __
12. slow   __ p __ __ __ y
13. different   __ i __ i __ __ r
14. determined   h __ __ i t __ __ t

Full   **Empty**

C. **Match the synonyms.**

1. inflate _____
2. operate _____
3. native _____
4. please _____
5. protect _____
6. chat _____
7. analyze _____
8. count _____
9. wizardry _____
10. prognosis _____
11. specimen _____
12. abandon _____

A. inhabitant
B. talk
C. magic
D. vacate
E. run
F. delight
G. compute
H. prediction
I. enlarge
J. defend
K. examine
L. sample

D. **Replace the italicized words in parentheses with synonyms from the machine. Write the synonyms on the lines.**

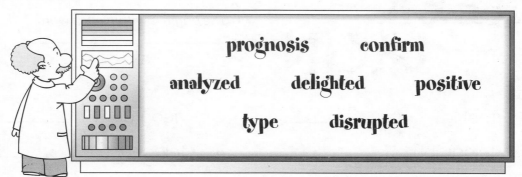

prognosis   confirm

analyzed   delighted   positive

type   disrupted

1. The scientist (*examined*) _____ the cells under the microscope carefully to (*determine*) _____ their (*classification*) _____ .

2. The (*prediction*) _____ of the patient's operation seemed (*good*) _____ .

3. Her parents were (*pleased*) _____ with her performance.

4. The unexpected task (*upset*) _____ my plan.

E.   Match the definitions with the words.

1.   virtuous   _____   (A) clever movement

2.   precise   _____   (B) slept

3.   beneficial   _____   (C) thought about, considered

4.   reflected   _____   (D) dedicated

5.   peculiar   _____   (E) kind, good, well meaning, honest

6.   conspicuous   _____   (F) useful, good

7.   ardent   _____   (G) odd, different, unique

8.   mammoth   _____   (H) exact, detailed

9.   docile   _____   (I) obvious, out in the open, in full view

10. slumbered   _____   (J) huge, overpowering

11. agile   _____   (K) peaceful, gentle, obedient

12. manoeuvre   _____   (L) athletic, well balanced, physically able

F.   Write the Greek or Latin origin for each of the following words.

GREEK
LATIN

The origin is within each word.

1.   metric   _____   2.   geography   _____

3.   telegraph   _____   4.   telephone   _____

5.   sympathy   _____   6.   physical   _____

7.   biological   _____   8.   botanical   _____

9.   auditorium   _____   10. manual   _____

11. operation   _____   12. subscribe   _____

13. jury   _____   14. video   _____

15. beneficial   _____   16. dictionary _____

G. Match each of the following derivative words with its definition.

1. hemisphere _____ A. go against, have an opposite opinion
2. monorail _____ B. lower the worth of something
3. century _____ C. predict as in the weather
4. kilometre _____ D. the time after the battle
5. contradict _____ E. be confused, unable to comprehend
6. depart _____ F. train on one track
7. devaluate _____ G. unit of 1,000 parts
8. misunderstand _____ H. leave
9. forecast _____ I. half of the earth
10. postwar _____ J. unit of 100 parts

H. Match the words formed with noun suffixes with their definitions.

1. kingdom _____ A. being a parent
2. happiness _____ B. actor
3. ownership _____ C. the opposition
4. performer _____ D. one who opposes you
5. competition _____ E. nothing in common, unalike
6. fatherhood _____ F. occurrence, a happening as a result of
7. circumstance _____ G. strong feeling of sorrow
8. difference _____ H. to be in possession of something
9. compassion _____ I. feeling of joy
10. competitor _____ J. the land belonging to royalty

ISBN: 978-1-897457-06-1

I.   **Match the following verbs with the definitions.**

1.	utilize	_____	(A) make or build
2.	verify	_____	(B) feel sorrow for
3.	negotiate	_____	(C) make clear or easy to understand
4.	hasten	_____	(D) use
5.	sympathize	_____	(E) untie
6.	create	_____	(F) make a deal
7.	simplify	_____	(G) hurry up, go quickly
8.	loosen	_____	(H) prove that something is true

J.   **Match the following adjectives with the definitions.**

1.	fantastic	_____	A. popular as with clothing
2.	useless	_____	B. shy
3.	partial	_____	C. dependable
4.	scrumptious	_____	D. full of energy
5.	active	_____	E. has no purpose
6.	reliable	_____	F. a part of, incomplete
7.	bashful	_____	G. delicious
8.	stylish	_____	H. incredible, amazing

K.   **Check the root word (underlined) of each of the following words to determine its meaning. Match the definition from the list.**

1.	<u>audi</u>ble	_____	A. study of stars and planets
2.	<u>bene</u>factor	_____	B. lawmaker, tyrant
3.	in<u>scrip</u>tion	_____	C. sad, pitiful
4.	<u>pa</u>thetic	_____	D. put off until later, afterwards

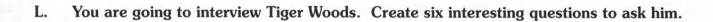

5. <u>astro</u>nomy _____

6. <u>post</u>pone _____

7. <u>dict</u>ator _____

8. <u>v</u>isualize _____

E. imagine, create a picture of

F. written note

G. can be heard

H. someone who does good for others

L. You are going to interview Tiger Woods. Create six interesting questions to ask him.

Born on December 30, 1975, Tiger Woods took an interest in golf at the age of 6 months, watching as his father hit golf balls into a net and imitating his swing. Tiger played in his first professional tournament in 1992 at age 16. Since then, he has had an impressive career. He is the career victories leader among active players on the PGA Tour.

1. _____

2. _____

3. _____

4. _____

5. _____

6. _____

ISBN: 978-1-897457-06-1

ISBN: 978-1-897457-06-1

1

Complete the 8 slides to flip your hand to show your palm. Change only one letter for each slide.

hand

h [ ] n d

[ ] [ ] [ ] [ ]

w i n [ ]

[ ] [ ] [ ] [ ]

[ ] i n e

[ ] [ ] [ ] [ ]

p a [ ] e

[ ] [ ] [ ] [ ]

ISBN: 978-1-897457-06-1

2 Danny the Duck wants to make some friends. Write the names of the sea animals that he wants to make friends with.

ISBN: 978-1-897457-06-1

Synonym Crossword Puzzle

Across

A. outstanding
B. talented
C. work
D. accomplish
E. plenty
F. anger

Down

1. strong
2. happiness
3. enough
4. weak
5. astonished
6. tired

4 Add a word to the end of the word on the left and the beginning of the word on the right to form two compound words.

1. dog   _____ wife

2. net   _____ shop

3. star   _____ house

4. rain   _____ man

5. home   _____ mark

6. wild   _____ time

5 Circle twelve sports in the Sports Word Search.

SPORTS WORD SEARCH

c	i	p	r	k	m	a	h	b	h	i	e	f	o
g	o	a	u	d	e	c	a	n	o	e	i	n	g
n	k	q	v	h	r	l	d	i	c	c	g	b	p
b	b	a	s	e	b	a	l	l	k	r	u	n	c
a	v	j	w	g	y	c	z	x	e	m	t	s	y
d	o	l	i	j	k	i	t	b	y	v	s	d	c
m	l	c	m	b	a	s	k	e	t	b	a	l	l
i	l	e	m	o	e	n	w	v	n	y	c	p	i
n	e	o	i	a	r	s	g	k	z	n	t	m	n
t	y	s	n	o	w	b	o	a	r	d	i	n	g
o	b	d	g	o	v	j	l	c	w	x	y	s	b
n	a	s	y	s	z	d	f	l	c	u	a	f	g
b	l	h	k	q	t	n	c	x	d	e	r	t	p
f	l	b	j	l	e	w	u	f	q	c	r	m	h

ISBN: 978-1-897457-06-1

Complete the 7 slides to turn "fish" into "love". Change only one letter for each slide.

7

Complete the crossword puzzle with antonyms of the clue words.

Antonym Crossword Puzzle

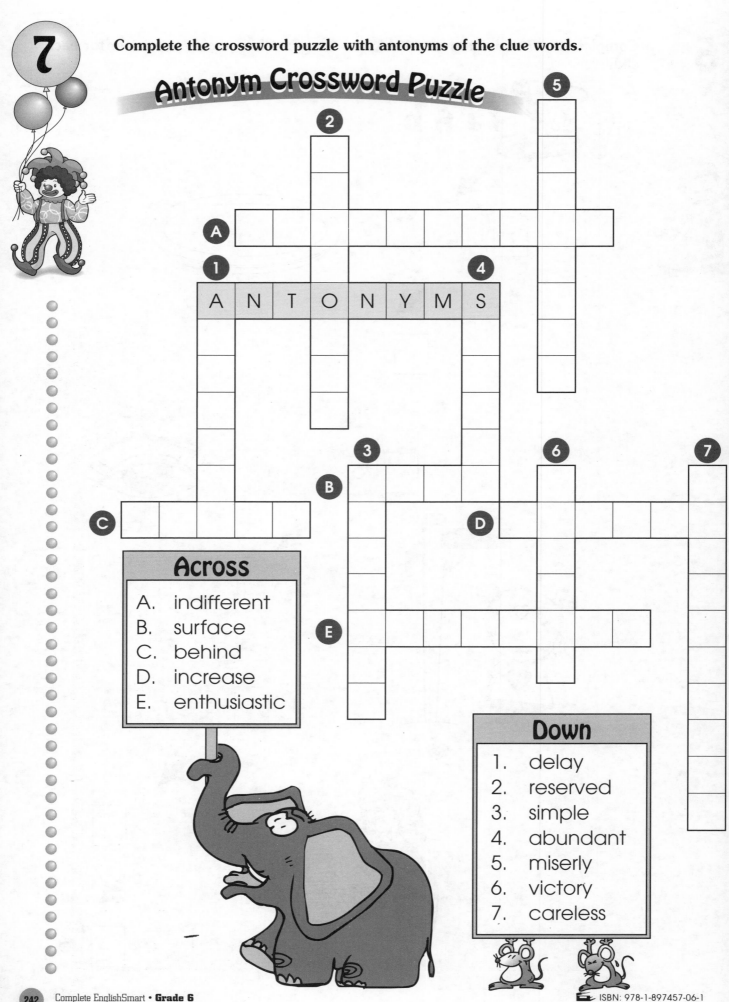

A N T O N Y M S

Across

A. indifferent
B. surface
C. behind
D. increase
E. enthusiastic

Down

1. delay
2. reserved
3. simple
4. abundant
5. miserly
6. victory
7. careless

ISBN: 978-1-897457-06-1

8

Circle fifteen animals or things that can fly in the "Flying" Word Search.

"Flying" Word Search

c	d	k	e	m	a	s	w	a	l	l	o	w	c
b	u	m	b	l	e	b	e	e	g	m	j	p	f
h	a	l	g	i	r	p	m	d	f	p	a	e	k
g	i	t	b	l	o	n	e	r	o	s	t	l	i
c	p	m	o	n	p	x	q	h	v	p	z	i	l
l	i	a	q	e	l	v	w	u	j	a	y	c	n
a	g	f	s	p	a	r	r	o	w	c	j	a	h
d	e	l	n	s	n	g	t	c	a	e	o	n	j
y	o	d	p	h	e	k	l	t	q	s	p	m	e
b	n	o	i	q	y	f	r	e	q	h	g	n	f
u	b	h	u	m	m	i	n	g	b	i	r	d	a
g	k	i	m	l	r	k	p	o	h	p	d	o	e
j	b	u	t	t	e	r	f	l	y	s	j	w	b
d	e	a	g	b	d	r	a	g	o	n	f	l	y

9

Look at the pictures. Complete the crossword puzzle.

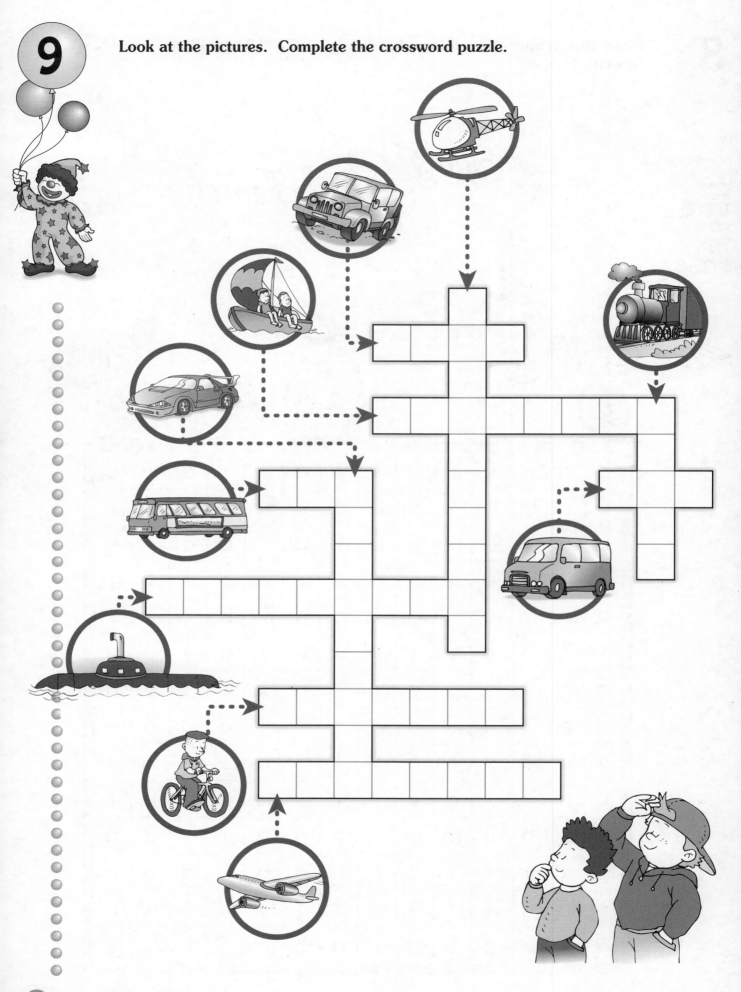

ISBN: 978-1-897457-06-1

10 Build the pyramid using letters in the word "TEA" to complete the words. The letters can be used more than once.

				A				
			B					
				G				
				P				
	G	R						
	R		P					
W				H		R		
P	L		S		N			
S				M		N		
		N	D		N	C		

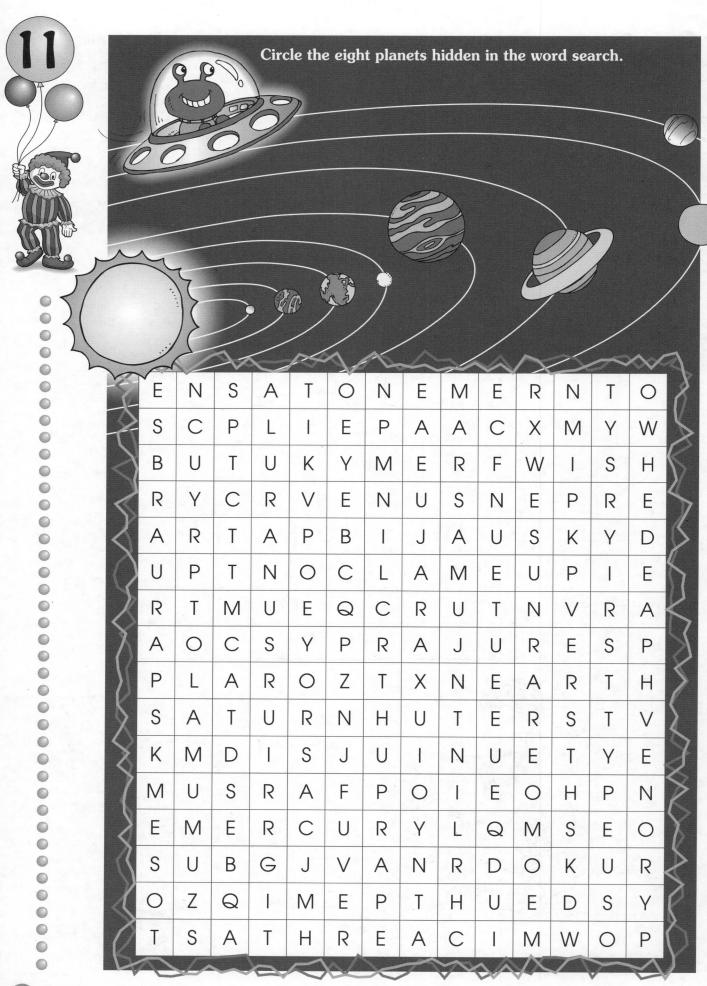

Circle the eight planets hidden in the word search.

E	N	S	A	T	O	N	E	M	E	R	N	T	O
S	C	P	L	I	E	P	A	A	C	X	M	Y	W
B	U	T	U	K	Y	M	E	R	F	W	I	S	H
R	Y	C	R	V	E	N	U	S	N	E	P	R	E
A	R	T	A	P	B	I	J	A	U	S	K	Y	D
U	P	T	N	O	C	L	A	M	E	U	P	I	E
R	T	M	U	E	Q	C	R	U	T	N	V	R	A
A	O	C	S	Y	P	R	A	J	U	R	E	S	P
P	L	A	R	O	Z	T	X	N	E	A	R	T	H
S	A	T	U	R	N	H	U	T	E	R	S	T	V
K	M	D	I	S	J	U	I	N	U	E	T	Y	E
M	U	S	R	A	F	P	O	I	E	O	H	P	N
E	M	E	R	C	U	R	Y	L	Q	M	S	E	O
S	U	B	G	J	V	A	N	R	D	O	K	U	R
O	Z	Q	I	M	E	P	T	H	U	E	D	S	Y
T	S	A	T	H	R	E	A	C	I	M	W	O	P

ISBN: 978-1-897457-06-1

Help Nellie get the trophy by giving an example in each box.

A  **1**-syllable word

A **2**-syllable word

A **3**-syllable word

A **4**-syllable word

A **5**-syllable word

A **6**-syllable word

1st

ISBN: 978-1-897457-06-1

13

Complete the crossword puzzle with synonyms of the clue words.

Synonym Crossword Puzzle

Across

A. fierce
B. delay
C. complete
D. sly
E. live
F. annoyed

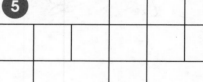

Down

1. depressed
2. consider
3. neglect
4. weak
5. quiet
6. cloudy
7. faint

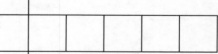

ISBN: 978-1-897457-06-1

14 Help Benny Bear find his pot of honey by colouring the hexagons with words that rhyme with "bear".

15 Colour the squirrels and acorns with words that rhyme the same colour.

brief

salt

tower

pour

bought

halt

leaf

sour

caught

soar

ISBN: 978-1-897457-06-1

16

Make words by matching the word parts in the three columns. Write the words on the lines.

1. dis • • logic • • ion

2. pre • • appear • • ance

3. in • • reason • • er

4. im • • view • • ly

5. il • • effect • • ment

6. un • • perfect • • al

7. sub • • arrange • • ive

8. inter • • conscious • • able

1. _____ 2. _____

3. _____ 4. _____

5. _____ 6. _____

7. _____ 8. _____

ISBN: 978-1-897457-06-1

1 The Monarch Butterfly

A. 1. T 2. F
3. T 4. F
5. F 6. T
7. F 8. F

B. (Suggested answers)
1. The great mystery surrounding the Monarch butterfly is that it travels up to 3,000 km one way to reach its winter roosts.
2. The Monarch starts as a caterpillar and becomes a pupa. The pupa then changes to a chrysalis state with hard skin. Finally, it emerges as a full-grown adult butterfly.

C. 1. The Monarch butterfly|(is) a member of the Danaidae family.
2. The new watch|(failed) to keep accurate time.
3. The cat|(chased) the mouse around the living room.
4. The students|(assembled) in the gymnasium for a presentation.
5. Hard work|often (results) in success.
6. The girl in a pink T-shirt and blue jeans|(is) my sister.
7. John and Tom|(walked) home from school together every day.
8. The man over there|(told) me to give you this form.
9. Last Sunday, my parents and I|(dined) at a French restaurant.
10. Riding in the car with the window open|(was) his dog's favourite pastime.

D.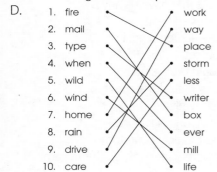
1. fire
2. mail
3. type
4. when
5. wild
6. wind
7. home
8. rain
9. drive
10. care

work
way
place
storm
less
writer
box
ever
mill
life

E. (Suggested answers)
fire : firewood, campfire, firefly, fireworks, wildfire
home : homesick, homeland, hometown, homegrown, homecoming

2 Foxes, the New City Dwellers

A. 1. wolves and dogs
2. by night
3. the red fox
4. 10 km

5. earth
6. rabbits, mice, and squirrels
7. 10 to 12 years
8. up to 50 km per hour
9. wild fruit and grass
10. retraces its steps and hides in trees

B. (Individual writing)

C. 1. The pianist played the piano (for) all the people.
2. He sat (in) the kitchen and ate the entire cake (by) himself.
3. He kicked the football (through) the goal posts.
4. The members (of) the team played hockey (against) another team.
5. He enjoyed the movie (with) the scary ending.
6. Get the ball before it goes (on) the road.
7. (Of) all (of) her friends, she liked Susan the best.
8. (In) the middle (of) the night, he woke up all the neighbours.
9. John and Anne were late (for) school.
10. Never before had he worried so much (about) his school grades.
11. Please put this box (into) the drawer.
12. He is thinking (of) an interesting title (for) his new book.

D. 1. inappropriate 2. review
3. disrespect 4. undependable
5. independent 6. reform
7. immature 8. displeased
9. uncertain 10. suburban
11. unreliable 12. distasteful
13. uncommon 14. retell
15. disregard 16. disbelief

3 "The Great One" – Wayne Gretzky (1)

A. 1. six 2. his father
3. ten 4. one
5. Gordie Howe 6. eighteen
7. two hundred fifteen

B. (Answers will vary.)

C. 1. where the Toyland was located ; Obj.
2. what you told me to do ; Obj.
3. what they did ; Obj. of prep.
4. that his name not be used ; Obj.
5. Whatever choice is made ; Subj.
6. how we could get to the destination ; Obj.
7. how we are rewarded ; Obj. of prep.
8. What he had said in the meeting ; Subj.
9. how I can avoid the problem ; Obj.
10. what the program is about ; Obj. of prep.

D. 1. debut 2. shatter
3. compensate 4. instilled
5. oversized 6. prodigy
7. opportunity 8. insurmountable

9. avid
10. consecutive
11. incorporated
12. surpassing
13. imitating
14. astounding
15. milestone

4 "The Great One" – Wayne Gretzky (2)

A. (Suggested answers)

Paragraph One: Gretzky led the Los Angeles Kings to the Stanley Cup Finals and boosted the attendance at home games.

Paragraph Two: In a Celtics-Lakers basketball game, Gretzky met Janet Jones, who later became his wife.

Paragraph Three: Gretzky expressed admiration for past and present hockey greats and listed five players for his personal All-Star Team.

Paragraph Four: Gretzky had the uncanny ability to control the offence of the game, which made him such a great player.

B. (Individual answers)

C.
1. adj. ; adv. ; adj.
2. adj. ; adv.
3. adj. ; adj.
4. adj. ; adj.
5. adj. ; adv.
6. adj. ; adv. ; adj.
7. adj. ; adv. ; adj.
8. adj. ; adj. ; adj.

D. (Order may vary.)
1. losing ; adj.
2. few ; adj.
3. ever ; adv.
4. future ; adj.
5. always ; adv.
6. openly ; adv.
7. personal ; adj.
8. uncanny ; adj.
9. pinpoint ; adj.
10. total ; adj.

E.

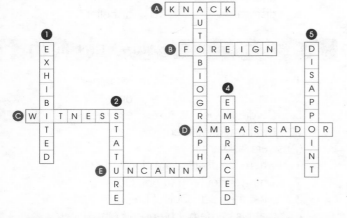

5 Johannes Gutenberg – the Pioneer of the Printing Press

A.
1. Books could be printed.
2. goldsmith
3. wealthy family
4. movable type
5. Strasbourg
6. metalwork
7. 1456
8. 300
9. He was relieved of his duty.

B.
1. into the classroom ; adv.
2. for playing games ; adv.
3. from the private school ; adj.
4. of St. Mary's ; adj.
5. in the car ; adj.
6. in the back seat ; adv.
7. in the yard ; adv.
8. under the couch ; adv.

C.
1. into
2. for
3. from
4. of
5. in
6. in
7. in
8. under

D.
1. wickedly
2. simply
3. purely
4. confinement
5. glorious
6. treacherous
7. definitely
8. discovery
9. invention
10. heavily
11. happiness
12. performance
13. creative
14. majority
15. reality
16. anchorage

6 Left Brain, Right Brain

A. (Answers will vary.)

B.
1. lateralization
2. hemispheres
3. 12%
4. 10%
5. touch
6. right
7. left

C.
1. before I arrived at school
2. Whenever I exercise
3. After I ran up the hill
4. which I got as a birthday gift
5. Before the teacher gave us any clues
6. although it was still early
7. Whenever he scored a goal
8. until the sun set
9. so that it could be shared
10. unless you start studying now
11. since he was twelve
12. Now that everyone has gone
13. because the project is due tomorrow
14. While they were halfway through the game

D.
1. unique
2. visual
3. determine
4. experiment
5. population
6. stationary
7. perception
8. hemispheres
9. lateralization

7 The Jackie Robinson Story (1)

A.
1. F
2. F
3. F
4. O
5. F
6. O
7. O
8. F
9. O
10. O
11. F
12. O

B. (Answer will vary.)
C. 1. C 2. C 3. F 4. F
5. C 6. F 7. F 8. C
9. F 10. C
D. (Individual writing)
E. 1. appear 2. unknown
3. poor 4. dull
5. unsociable 6. flexible
F. 1. antibody 2. antisocial
3. antiseptic 4. antifreeze
5. anti-aircraft

8 The Jackie Robinson Story (2)

A. 1. In California, Robinson attended Pasadena Junior College where he set records in track and field, quarterbacked the football team, and led the basketball team in scoring.
2. When he joined the Kansas City Monarchs of the Negro League, he was finally being paid to do what he did best.
3. Branch Rickey, a forward-thinking Dodger manager, signed Jackie Robinson to a contract and sent him to play for the Montreal Royals, a Dodger farm team.
4. Jackie answered the public scorn by winning the Rookie of the Year in 1947 and going on to help the Dodgers win six pennants in ten years.
B. (Answers will vary.)
C. 1. Did she forget about the party or was she sick?
2. The cat chased the birds and they flew away at once.
3. The storm lasted all night and we stayed awake.
4. He should hurry or he will be late.
5. Sometimes you win and sometimes you lose.
6. The players tried hard but they lost the game anyway.
7. Some students went out for lunch and others stayed at school.
8. You can't cure a cold but you can take medicine for relief.
9. You can buy the new game but you have to pay for it yourself.
D. 1. read 2. watt
3. great 4. sale
5. brake 6. feat
7. pours 8. bear
E.

9 Leonardo da Vinci – Artist and Visionary

A. 1. B 2. C 3. A 4. C
5. B 6. A
B. 1. The boy fell off the swing because he was pushed.
2. The money was found after I looked everywhere. / After I looked everywhere, the money was found.
3. The girls played in the yard when it was recess. / When it was recess, the girls played in the yard.
4. The tourists looked on as the farmer crossed the road with his sheep. / As the farmer crossed the road with his sheep, the tourists looked on.
5. The fans cheered wildly whenever the team scored a goal. / Whenever the team scored a goal, the fans cheered wildly.
6. My car was very clean before it rained. / Before it rained, my car was very clean.
7. Although the test was easy, she went over all her answers again. / She went over all her answers again although the test was easy.
8. While the children were playing, someone knocked on the door. / Someone knocked on the door while the children were playing.
C. (Answers will vary.)

Progress Test 1

A. 1. F 2. F 3. T 4. T
5. T 6. F 7. T 8. F
9. T 10. T 11. T 12. T
13. F 14. F 15. F
B. 1. B 2. B 3. A 4. C
5. B 6. C 7. B 8. C
9. A
C. 1. train ; (flew)
2. Boys ; girls ; (played)
3. animals ; (slept)
4. boy ; (collapsed)
5. students ; (were)
D. 1. (Whoever makes the decision)
2. (what the question was)
3. (whomever had the best information)
4. (what you said last night)
5. (How you figure out the answer to the math question)
E. 1. of the team ; (into the dressing room)
2. at the local school ; (at the fair)
3. (In all her years of teaching)
4. (In the dark of night) ; from the crowd
F. 1. F 2. C
3. C 4. C
5. F

Section 1 Answers

G. 1. compound   2. complex
   3. compound   4. compound
   5. compound   6. complex
   7. complex   8. complex

H. 1. impossible   2. misspelled
   3. undependable   4. immature
   5. unnecessary   6. untrue

I. 1. possibility   2. simply
   3. attachment   4. glorious
   5. treacherous   6. truly

J. 1. ignorant   2. destroy
   3. useless   4. safe
   5. rough

K.

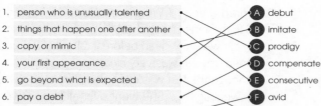

1. person who is unusually talented — C prodigy
2. things that happen one after another — E consecutive
3. copy or mimic — B imitate
4. your first appearance — A debut
5. go beyond what is expected — G surpass
6. pay a debt — D compensate
7. be enthusiastic — F avid

L. 1. suitcase   2. corrections
   3. curiosity   4. pride
   5. destruction   6. joyful
   7. homework   8. fireplace
   9. useless   10. unknown

10 Guinness World Records

A. 1. 1759   2. Arthur
   3. London   4. 151
   5. 1955   6. promotional
   7. Dublin   8. licensees
   9. 100   10. 73

B. (Suggested answers)
1. Pub patrons liked disputing facts on various topics and it would help if there was a book with definitive answers to such arguments.
2. People worldwide crave the knowledge of seemingly insignificant facts.

C. (Individual writing)

D.

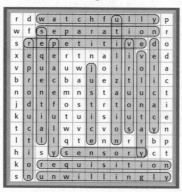

11 English – the Language of the World

A. 1. O   2. O   3. F   4. F
   5. O   6. O   7. F   8. F

B. (Answers will vary.)

C. 1. !   2. ?   3. .   4. ?
   5. !   6. .   7. !   8. ?

D. The students, the teachers, and the parents attended the winter carnival. Although there was not very much snow, there was a snow sculpturing contest. They ate hot dogs, muffins, and cakes, and they enjoyed hot chocolate, Coca-Cola, and a variety of juices. The principal, Mr. Johnson, an avid skater, showed off his skill at the rink. The grade eight students organized the games, arranged the contests, supervised the younger students, and set up the signs. One student asked enthusiastically, "Could we do this again next year?"

E. 1. create   2. popular
   3. inscription   4. reaction
   5. galloping   6. Tighten
   7. wishful   8. version
   9. successful   10. adventurous

12 No More Pencils...No More Books

A. 1. The transistor was invented.
2. New computers with expanded memory capabilities operating at high speeds were created.
3. The need to store mathematical information was recognized.
4. It had to be shut down regularly.
5. Technology was not available.
6. Smaller, faster, and cheaper computers became available.

B. (Individual writing)

C. 1. Where   2. birth
   3. besides   4. dyed
   5. accept   6. counsel
   7. canvass   8. between
   9. edition   10. clothes
   11. few   12. hung

13 The Great Pyramid of Ancient Egypt (1)

A. 1. B   2. A   3. A   4. B
   5. A   6. B

B. (Individual answer)

C. (Individual writing)

D. 1. compliance   2. sadness
   3. reliability   4. thoughtless
   5. impolitely   6. space
   7. outrage   8. announcement

9. waste
10. inability
11. respect
12. irresponsible
13. undeniable
14. instructor
15. can't

14 The Great Pyramid of Ancient Egypt (2)

A. 1. guests
2. firmness
3. Limestone
4. labourers
5. farms
6. mummified
7. sarcophagus
8. afterlife
9. Priests
10. landscape
11. ornamentation
12. construction
B. (Individual writing)
C. (Answers will vary.)
D. 1. is a bear
2. is the ligament
3. is the sunshine
4. of time
5. is the artery

15 Thomas Edison – the Greatest Inventor in History

A. 1. F
2. T
3. T
4. F
5. F
B. 1. He had difficulty following the lessons.
2. He used the time to read books and did experiments at home.
3. The smell from his laboratory was too strong.
4. He learned how to use the telegraph.
5. He decided to be a full-time inventor.
C. (Answer will vary.)
D. (Suggested answers)
1. I want to go to the park to have fun.
2. He noticed the key in the lock.
3. I really enjoy going to the movies.
4. Exercise is beneficial.
5. I think that the school year is too long.
6. Today is a holiday so most stores are closed.
7. I remember he won the championship last year.
8. The girl who is standing there with a dog is my classmate.
E. 1. frequently
2. problem
3. deeply
4. anticipated
5. begin
6. present
7. famous
8. inventions
F. 1. automatically
2. transmit
3. enjoyed
4. roving
5. adopted
6. excel
7. stop
8. leave

16 Accurate Measurement Was Not Always Accurate

A.

B. (Suggested answers)
1. Before Henry's declaration, the yard was the length of a girdle around the king's waist which would have increased greatly had they used the waistline of Henry VIII.
2. Conversions between various lengths and quantities are by multiplying or dividing by 10, 100, or 1000.
3. The switch would affect all aspects of life.
C. (Individual writing)
D. 1. ecstatic
2. scampered
3. visited
4. positioned
5. cavernous
E. 1. gentle
2. flowed
3. green
4. towering
5. leaned
6. swooped
7. enjoy
8. cool
9. refresh
10. peaceful

17 The Mystery of Flight 19 (1)

A. 1. F
2. T
3. F
4. T
5. T
6. F
7. T
8. F
9. F
B. 1. This part of the Atlantic is subject to sudden storms and the Gulf Stream can erase evidence of disasters swiftly. Also, the ocean floor there creates unpredictable marine conditions.
2. It was either the devil doing his handiwork or aliens that hurled the crafts into space.
3. (Individual answer)
C. (Suggested answers)
1. When the game was over, we left the arena together.
2. They were shopping for a gift but they could not find one they liked.

3. After the recess bell sounded, the schoolchildren played in the yard.
4. The dog barked at the mailman when he delivered the letters.
5. After the runners took their positions, the race was on.
6. Although the teacher spoke loudly, we still couldn't hear him.

D. (Individual writing)

18 The Mystery of Flight 19 (2)

A. (Suggested answers)
1. Five Avenger torpedo bombers left the Naval Air Station. Their mission was to practise bombing. None of the bombers returned.
2. One of the crew of Flight 19 stated on radio that he didn't know where he was. Lt. Taylor thought he was in the Florida Keys. Taylor was not in the Keys but likely in the Bahamas.
3. The navy plane in search of Flight 19 also disappeared. Fort Lauderdale Naval Base became increasingly concerned for the safety of the crews. No trace of Flight 19 or the search plane was ever found.

B. (Individual answers)

C.
1.	massacre	2.	monitor
3.	lives	4.	forty
5.	heroes	6.	barely
7.	government	8.	existence
9.	seize	10.	athletic
11.	beautiful	12.	whether
13.	ninth	14.	necessary
15.	independent	16.	kangaroo
17.	comparison	18.	truly
19.	embarrassed	20.	luckily
21.	occasion	22.	develop
23.	skiing	24.	accommodate
25.	tuition	26.	video

D. (Individual writing)

Progress Test 2

A.
1.	beer	2.	500,000
3.	1946	4.	gods
5.	Romans	6.	railway
7.	23	8.	14
9.	2,700	10.	ENIAC

B.
1.	T	2.	T	3.	F	4.	F
5.	T	6.	T	7.	F	8.	F
9.	T	10.	T	11.	T	12.	F
13.	T	14.	F	15.	F	16.	F
17.	T						

C. (Suggested answers)
1. When Sharon was six, her family moved from Montreal to Toronto.
2. Charles likes his new bike very much and he rides it to the park every day.
3. The roads are slippery because it has been snowing in the past few days and people have to drive slowly.

D.
1. When I go sailing, I get seasick.
2. How many eggs do you need for the cake?
3. After you check in your luggage, you get your boarding pass.
4. Slow down! You are moving too fast.

E. (Suggested answers)
1. well-known ; unknown
2. anticipated ; unexpected
3. present ; old
4. hard ; easy
5. expensive ; cheap

F. (Suggested answers)
1. I want to go shopping.
2. If you study hard, you will be a success.
3. As the team did not have enough players, they defaulted the game and ended up losing.
4. The dog follows me wherever I go.

G. (Suggested answers)
1. I was walking home when it was raining and I got all wet.
2. The dog barked when the man knocked on the door; he was frightened.
3. It was 5:00 p.m. and the traffic was building; rush hour was upon us.
4. She was unhappy because she had lost her bracelet that her mother gave her.

H.
1.	except	2.	birth
3.	clothes	4.	where
5.	addition	6.	Beside
7.	canvas		

I.
1.	excitement	2.	beautiful
3.	creative	4.	slyly
5.	surprisingly	6.	loudness
7.	eruption		

J.
1.	population	2.	actor
3.	excitable	4.	kindness
5.	confidence	6.	reaction
7.	separation	8.	utility
9.	repetitious	10.	peacemaker
11.	virtuous	12.	unwilling
13.	delicacy	14.	undeniable
15.	disrespect		

1   Grammar Overview

A. 1. restaurant ; food
   2. Beauty ; eye ; beholder
   3. teacher ; poem ; friendship
   4. place
   5. house ; storm
   6. end ; sense ; emptiness

B. 1. What   2. he
   3. he   4. they
   5. him   6. He
   7. himself   8. this
   9. she   10. their

C. (Circle these verbs.)
know ; living ; reported ; been ; exists ; surfaced ; revealed ; turned ; caused ; hope

D. 1. difficult   2. national
   3. frigid   4. British
   5. frozen   6. silver
   7. amateur

E. 1. That performance was exceptionally good.
   2. It has been almost a year since we last saw him. / It has almost been a year since we last saw him.
   3. He was not good at that and did it rather oddly.
   4. The slope was steep and they had to go down cautiously.
   5. He nodded knowingly and started figuring out how to settle the matter.

F. 1. of   2. from
   3. to   4. on
   5. beyond   6. with
   7. for   8. to
   9. about

G. 1. although ; and   2. since / as / because
   3. unless   4. but
   5. since / as / because   6. if / when
   7. or ; but

H. 1. Oh no   2. Wow
   3. Great   4. Hey
   5. Hurray   6. Look out
   7. Yuck   8. Oops

2   Verbs

A. 1. The ripe apples were picked by the children.
   2. The careless driver was warned by the police officer.
   3. Sue borrowed the books for the project.
   4. The classroom will be decorated for the party by us.
   5. The puppy was left in the backyard by Darrel.

B. 1. IM   2. IN   3. IM
   4. IN   5. SUB

C. (Individual writing)

D. 1. How I wish Jane were here with us.
   2. We looked at him as though he were a monster.

3. If I were you, I would accept the offer right away.
4. Her parents demanded that she pay for the repair.
5. If Sam were the organizer, the show would be much better.

E. (Suggested writing)
1. Valerie's mother suggested that Valerie leave her project until the next day.
2. The doctor advises Mr. Sherwood that he get up earlier and exercise for half an hour before going to work.
3. The teacher demanded that Jeremy apologize to Patricia for his rudeness.
4. At the party, Janet socialized with everyone that came her way as if she were the hostess.
5. Mrs. Brown suggested that Julie read more if she wanted to have any improvement in comprehension.
6. If Debbie were taller, she would be able to ride on the roller-coaster.

3   Verbals

A. 1. to become ; I   2. swimming ; G
   3. cooling ; P   4. laughing ; P
   5. to see ; I   6. cooking ; G
   7. jogging ; G   8. crossing ; P
   9. To settle ; I   10. to leave ; I
   11. driving ; G

B. (Individual writing)

C. 1. a skiing trip
   2. Skiing downhill
   3. to keep my balance
   4. tobogganing more than skiing
   5. taking a rest
   6. many other beginning skiers
   7. Drinking a cup of hot chocolate ; the skiing lesson
   8. sitting in the snow
   9. something buried deep in the snow
   10. a torn mitten

D. 1. N   2. N   3. ADV
   4. ADJ   5. ADV

E. (Individual writing)

4   Phrases

A. 1. The red, sleek sports car ; an arrow
   2. The losing team ; a good fight ; the end
   3. the long, uphill climb
   4. a cool, refreshing drink ; the pool
   5. a warm and fun reception
   6. seven honour students ; our class
   7. a delicious cheesecake
   8. the fluffy, creepy thing
   9. The long, bumpy ride ; almost an hour
   10. No one ; that thick, oily substance
   11. All of us ; an extremely boring movie
   12. the most skilful player

B. 1. (of) the opposing team
2. (That afternoon) ; ((in) the compound)
3. ((through) the tunnel)
4. (of) the team
5. (from) his group
6. ((from) morning to night)
7. ((in) the hallway)
8. ((across) the ditch)
9. (in) the cooler
10. ((up) the tall tree)
11. (all (over) the place)
12. (of) the palace

C. 1. in the pool
2. on the bench
3. soft and beautiful
4. on weekends
5. very quickly
6. from the daycare centre

D. (Individual writing)

E. (Individual writing)

F. (Individual writing)

---

5 Direct and Indirect Speech

A. 1. Ted explained that the moon revolves around the Earth.
2. Mabel said that she liked the cotton dress more.
3. Fred's father said that he would attend the ceremony.
4. Karen said that she was never good at singing.
5. Ivan says that he always enjoys window-shopping with them.
6. Evelyn told Mrs. Wayne that they had tried many ways.

B. 1. Alex told his father that he had not played in the game the day before.
2. Ron said that it had happened a week before.
3. Molly said that her grandma would come two days later.
4. The waiter said that they served fresh seafood that day.
5. The teacher said that in the following week, there would be two new students in their class.
6. Bill said that they had gone to Hamilton the week before.

C. (Suggested writing)
1. Mrs. Watson asked Ben which was the one he wanted.
2. They asked when they could start.
3. The police officer asked if I had come that way.
4. She asked him if he was going with her the following day.
5. Mrs. Healey asked her neighbour whether he / she had seen her cat.
6. Angela asked the boy what his name was.
7. The lady asked the cashier how much she owed.

D. (Suggested writing)
1. "Can you take me to your school?" the woman asked them.
2. "Have you got an MP3 player?" Carol asked Bill.
3. "Is there anyone in the house?" asked the delivery man.
4. "Have you seen my Science book?" I asked him.
5. "Did you borrow the storybook?" the librarian asked me.
6. "Are you ready to order?" the waitress asked us.

E. (Suggested writing)
Felix said that they would have a game with Harry's team the following day but they had not quite prepared yet because a lot of his teammates were still busy with their projects and they did not have time for practice. He thought they would lose.

---

6 Clauses and Sentences

A. 1. IND   2. IND   3. D   4. D
5. IND   6. D   7. IND   8. IND
9. D   10. IND   11. D   12. IND

B. (Individual writing)

C. (Individual writing)

D. 1. C   2. C   3. CCX   4. CX
5. CCX   6. CCX   7. CX

E. (Individual writing)

F. (Individual writing)

G. (Individual writing)

Progress Test 1

A. 1. noun   2. preposition
3. verb   4. adjective
5. pronoun   6. interjection
7. adjective   8. conjunction
9. adverb   10. verb
11. adjective   12. pronoun
13. preposition

B. 1. The hills were climbed (by Rachel and Murphy).
2. Rachel heard a rustling sound.
3. Murphy discovered an old tree stump.
4. The grass behind the tree stump was sniffed (by Murphy).
5. Rachel called the dog.
6. Murphy ignored Rachel's call.

C. Imperative: 1 ; 3
Indicative: 4 ; 5
Subjunctive: 2

D. 1. infinitive   2. gerund
3. participle   4. infinitive
5. gerund   6. infinitive
7. participle

E. 1. a torn jacket
2. the barking dog
3. to leave the man alone
4. finding a leprechaun
5. making your wishes

F. 1. a small and strange looking man
2. imaginary characters
3. his curious expression
4. The leprechaun's name ; a lovely name
5. Rachel's first wish ; an easy decision
6. a giant, gooey cheesecake
7. Rachel's wasteful wish

8. The cake ; the grassy, green hills
9. the incredibly delicious treat
G. 1. too quickly
   2. in the grass
   3. from Canada
   4. deep front
   5. over the hills
H. (Suggested writing)
   1. Aunt Anne exclaimed that Rachel had almost missed dinner.
   2. Uncle Pat asked Rachel where she had been.
   3. Rachel explained that she had been playing outside with Murphy.
   4. Aunt Anne asked if / whether they should sit down and eat.
   5. Rachel said that she was not very hungry.
   6. Uncle Pat asked Rachel why she wasn't hungry since she hadn't had anything to eat.
   7. Rachel said that she was not feeling well and asked her aunt and uncle if / whether she could go to bed.
   8. Aunt Anne touched Rachel's forehead and said that Rachel didn't have a fever.
   9. Uncle Pat told Rachel to go ahead and said that she could eat later.
I. 1. CX   2. CCX   3. C
   4. C   5. C   6. CX
J. 1. Even though Seamus disapproved
   2. she saw it appear out of thin air
   3. Wherever I go
   4. You only have one wish left

7 Sentences

A. (Suggested writing)
   1. Jonathan watched a very interesting television show about dinosaurs. He asked his parents to take him to the museum so that he could learn more about dinosaurs.
   2. Jonathan brought his friend Matthew because Matthew likes dinosaurs, too. Matthew had never been to the museum before so he was very excited.
   3. After they visited all of the exhibits about dinosaurs, they stopped for lunch in the cafeteria. Since they were not tired, they visited the exhibits about ancient Egypt after lunch.
B. (Suggested writing)
   1. The Smiths went on a two-week vacation to Rome, Italy.
   2. Since it was Alex's birthday, Marjorie came to visit him and brought him a present and a cake.
   3. Since the cave was pitch dark and eerie, the children held their breaths and dared not make a sound.
C. (Suggested writing)
   1. My sister always wants to get the lead role and become famous.
   2. Weight gain is often the result of eating too much candy and junk food, and eating between meals.
   3. They think science projects are more interesting than English projects.

4. It is important to work hard and do well in school.
5. Her success was due to her perseverance, hard work, and the support from her family.
D. (Suggested writing)
   1. They baked a huge birthday cake specially for her.
   2. Posing as a tourist, the undercover police officer caught the pickpocket.
   3. My father earned almost two thousand dollars more for the additional work.
   4. She read with her sister the story about Little Ann.
   5. Talking to his mother, he caught sight of a spider.

8 Punctuation (1)

A. 1. The farmer gave us some carrots, a few apples, and a lot of potatoes.
   2. Did you see the sleek, blue sports car on the driveway?
   3. Mrs. Thomson, our next door neighbour, told us not to worry.
   4. Once we start, we should continue and not give up.
   5. Although I didn't see it happen, I could feel the horror.
   6. The little boy replied, "I just asked for some candies."
   7. Indeed, it was the best we could do for her.
   8. The incident happened on June 19, 2004.
   9. The storm left the village with flooded basements, fallen trees, and mudslides.
B. 1. Our dog, which everyone loves, likes eating snacks.
   4. On my way to school, I ran into Jim's mother, who told me that Jim was not feeling well.
   6. She let me see her camera, which was as thin as a credit card.
   11. Pam's younger sister, who looks very much like her, will come to the party too.
   12. Mrs. Steele, whose son is about my age, bakes great cookies.
C. 1. The chairman neglected one crucial fact: the report was not ready.
   2. The article "Travel in Asia: China and India" is an interesting read.
   3. We expect only one thing from him: complete the project by next Monday.
   4. They were told to pack these for the trip: a flashlight, a compass, and a radio.
   5. The company had the following openings: secretary, receptionist, administrative assistant.
   6. We all have the same goal: win the tournament this time.
   7. The old saying goes: "Blood is thicker than water."
   8. Do remember this: never ever give up.
D. 1. To prepare himself for the race, he performed the following exercises every day: weightlifting, which built his upper body strength; running, which built up his endurance; biking, which strengthened his leg muscles.
   2. They met with John; it was a brief meeting.
   3. He was introduced to the following people: Jason, Peter's cousin; Mandy, his boss's daughter; Sam, the secretary's husband.

4. It was chilly out there; the temperature dropped to a mere 2°C.
5. We tried our best to finish it on time; however, we couldn't make it.
6. She's such a popular athlete; wherever she goes, she's surrounded by fans.
7. He found himself face to face with someone he knew; it was Corey.
8. The surprise gift finally arrived; it was a nifty DVD player.
9. No one wanted to leave; they were all eager for the announcement.
10. We had a sumptuous dinner; everyone was full.

9 Punctuation (2)

A. 1. The final showdown – the do-or-die game – will be telecast live.
2. Everything boiled down to one word – perseverance.
3. The Greatest Game Ever Played – the story of an underdog golfer – is the best motivational film I have ever watched.
4. No matter what you do – explaining, pleading, or begging – it won't make her change her mind.

B. 1. The new manager is a twenty-three-year-old graduate.
2. This is a once-in-a-lifetime chance that you shouldn't miss.
3. Non-members are not allowed to go in the members-only lounge.
4. The semi-final for the above-eighteen contestants will start next week.
5. He lives in a twenty-five-year-old split-level bungalow.
6. A lot of people were inspired by his from-rags-to-riches story.
7. The report shows that two-thirds of the population are under fifty-five years of age.

C. 1. The new museum (see inset) will be officially opened on August 21, 2009.
2. The honour students (of which I am one) are invited to the ceremony.
3. The complimentary tickets (a pair from Uncle Charlie and another pair from Mr. Todd) came just in time.
4. They should (a) get a form, (b) fill it out, (c) get their parents' consent, and (d) return it to their teacher before noon tomorrow.
5. The merger (yet to be confirmed) is said to take effect in January 2010.
6. The graph (Fig. 2b) shows the population growth over the past 20 years.
7. The series (2-2) would be decided in the final game to be played this afternoon.
8. The supporting role (Captain Truman) was given to a little-known actor by the name of Willie Whitt.

D. 1. Recent research indicates that most of the asteroids orbit around...the chance that an asteroid strikes the Earth is one in a million.
2. Malls sprout up in big cities due to...the largest shopping centre in the world is the West Edmonton Mall in Edmonton.
3. Malawi is an impoverished third world country in Africa. The infant mortality rate...the average life expectancy is only 37 years.
4. There are many ways to conserve energy...with more and more people switching to driving smaller cars which are more fuel-efficient.
5. Roberta Bondar became the first female astronaut to go into space. She received the Order of Canada...in 1998, Roberta was named to the Canadian Medical Hall of Fame.
6. The cell phone has become almost an indispensable gadget ...the government is beginning to look into regulating the use of the cell phone.
7. A Great White ranges from five to seven metres in length and weighs...swimming at a speed of 16 to 20 km per hour, the Great White usually attacks its prey from behind or beneath.

10 Root Words, Prefixes, and Suffixes

A. 1. unable ; ability
2. tolerable / tolerant ; toleration / tolerance
3. quicken ; quickly
4. infertile ; fertility
5. informal ; formality
6. unsuccessful ; success

B. 1. cover
2. seem
3. divide
4. probable
5. monument
6. adventure
7. act
8. ordinary
9. satisfy
10. sport

C. 1. submerged
2. outsmart
3. anti-government
4. dissatisfied
5. predawn
6. impossible
7. misunderstand
8. outnumber
9. miscalculate
10. hyperactive
11. unfit

D. 1. thankful
2. lightly
3. clueless
4. responsive
5. categorize
6. logical
7. payable
8. darkness
9. strongly
10. realize

E. 1. disapprove
2. quickly
3. strangeness
4. subzero
5. impatient
6. fantasize

F. (Suggested answers)
1. helpful ; helpless
2. untrue ; truthful
3. lovely ; lovable
4. redo ; doable
5. misbehave ; behaviour

6. definitely ; indefinite
7. honesty ; dishonest
8. indirect ; directly

11 Homonyms, Synonyms, and Antonyms

A. 1. pour
   2. theirs
   3. mussels
   4. sell
   5. whether

B. 1. time ; thyme   2. flee ; flea
   3. knight ; night   4. coarse ; course

C.

D. (Suggested answers)
   1. angry
   2. embarrassed
   3. delighted
   4. soaked
   5. serious
   6. sensitive
   7. chilly ; trembled
   8. exhausted
   9. frightening ; courageous

E. (Suggested writing)
   1. The naughty boy climbed up the tall tree with ease.
   2. The ballerina danced gracefully and earned thunderous applause.
   3. Two beavers were swimming in the murky water.
   4. The town became depressed after the Gold Rush.
   5. We strolled leisurely down the tranquil road.
   6. Marie screamed loudly on the roller-coaster ride.
   7. The rumblings from the machine are annoying.
   8. Keith is a cheerful and sociable boy.
   9. Mr. Moore cannot fall asleep unless the room is completely dark.
   10. He couldn't remove the writing because he had used a permanent marker.

12 Troubleshooting Confusing Writing

A. (Suggested writing)
   1. Andrew asked Peter to explain Peter's problem.
   2. Ian and Joe worked on a puzzle and Joe finished it first.
   3. The girls in grade six competed against the boys and the boys lost.
   4. Rob met Sam when Sam first joined the school team.
   5. Matt argued with Paul and Matt was furious.
   6. Janice told her best friend Mandy that Janice had won the first prize.
   7. The Jays and the Yankees each scored a run in the seventh inning, and the Jays were confident that they would tie the game soon.

B. (Suggested writing)
   1. Last Sunday, he talked endlessly about his exciting trip.
   2. She spent almost all of her savings. Now she is poor.
   3. After he was rescued, he told his family about his brush with death.
   4. Mike being the youngest in the family, no one listens to him.
   5. Laughing out loud, the children were entertained by the naughty monkey.
   6. Walking to school, he saw Ashley and her dog.
   7. Standing on the riverbank, the children spotted a big fish.

C. 1. likes   2. are
   3. is   4. knows
   5. All   6. spells
   7. are   8. was
   9. practises   10. have
   11. One   12. Several

D. 2. Either you or I am eligible for the scholarship.
   3. The coach, as well as the players, was very disappointed with the decision.
   4. Each of the children was given a basket of strawberries.
   6. Neither the class nor the teacher has heard of the news.
   7. None of the committee members was prepared to vote.
   8. Has any one of you met our new principal before?
   10. Someone holding three parcels at the door wants to talk to you.
   11. Everyone attending the wedding ceremony was happy for them.

13 Add Colour to Your Writing

A. (Suggested writing)
   1. Over the plain a crimson sun set.
   2. In the locker room assembled the players for a pep talk.
   3. Fish and chips was what she wanted to eat.
   4. To avoid the tag, he moved deftly to the side.
   5. To save her from the flood, the firefighters raced against time.
   6. Through the narrow alley sped the motorbike.
   7. With two out and one on third base, he scored the winning run.
   8. In the breeze flew gracefully the kites.

B. (Individual writing)

C. (Individual writing)

D. 1. petrified   2. drained
    3. considerate   4. inexperienced
    5. towering

E. (Individual writing)

F. (Suggested writing)
1. The girls can ski but would rather not.
2. I don't think it is proper to do that.
3. Mother said it was necessary for us to come home for dinner.
4. She doesn't seem to realize the crux of the problem.
5. They were all eager to take part in it.
6. The ferry to Charlottetown starts here.
7. We finish school at 3:30 p.m.
8. I may be late if I don't hurry.

Progress Test 2

A. (Suggested answers)

Rachel was very excited about her shiny, red bicycle; she had never owned a bicycle before. "I can't wait to take it into town tomorrow!" Rachel exclaimed. "There are three places I really want to go to: the library, the bakery, and the toy store."

"I think that you are forgetting something," said Seamus. Rachel looked at him strangely. She couldn't imagine what he meant.

"Oh! Thank you, Seamus for the cake and the bike!" she said.

"You're welcome but that's not what I mean," he said. "Don't you think your aunt and uncle are going to wonder where this bicycle came from?"

"I guess I will tell them about finding you," said Rachel.

"I don't think that's a good idea," said Seamus. "They can't see me – only children can see me. If you tell them about me, they might think there is something wrong with you."

"I know what to do! I'll bring it outside when they are asleep. I will hide it somewhere on the property," said Rachel.

Seamus didn't think this was a good idea but he did not want to argue. He went to sleep in the shoebox Rachel had put out for him. Rachel stayed awake until she heard her aunt and uncle go to bed.

B. (Suggested answers)
1. Rachel slowly carried the bicycle down the twenty-six stairs.
2. She noticed a shed (her uncle built it five years ago) which looked old and rickety.
3. Rachel thought of many different places – the shed, the ditch, and even Murphy's doghouse – but she settled on hiding it inside some bushes.
4. Morning finally came – the moment she had been waiting for – and Rachel got ready to go out and ride her bicycle.

5. She thought of Fiona (Rachel's best friend) who has a bicycle just like this one.
6. Fiona is an eleven-year-old girl.
7. It didn't matter to Rachel what the weather was like – rainy, foggy, or windy – she wasn't going to let anything stop her from riding her bicycle.

C. 1. quickly   2. comfortable
    3. responsive   4. indirect
    5. subtitle   6. careless
    7. unaware

D. 1. conscious   2. belief
    3. believe   4. caution
    5. understand

E. 1. route   2. way
    3. piece   4. course
    5. one   6. right

F. (Suggested answers)
1. considered   2. nervously
3. stole   4. final
5. certain

G. 1. pleased   2. lifted
    3. down   4. carefully
    5. slowly   6. asleep

H. 1. walk   2. walks
    3. sits   4. begins ; arrive
    5. is   6. are
    7. sees

I. 1. glimmering   2. glared
    3. stole   4. astonished
    5. explained

J. (Suggested writing)
1. Rachel was a bit confused because she thought Seamus had given her that bicycle.
2. Seamus told Rachel that the bicycle was taken because bicycles did not just appear out of nowhere.
3. Now Rachel understood that she should have been more careful with her wishes.

1 Creating an Interesting Story Ending

A. (Individual writing)
B. Paragraph 1 : B
   Paragraph 2 : A
   Paragraph 3 : A
C. 1. trivia 2. shocked 3. eerie
   4. anticipation 5. brush 6. scurried
D. (Answers will vary.)
   1. Time : the last weekend in May; they packed on a Thursday night to get an early start on Friday
      Place : the Fernandez cottage
   2. Events :
      a. trees cast eerie shadows
      b. animal scurried into the brush
      Descriptions : (Any 2)
      – moon was bright in the dark sky
      – silver light on the cottage road
      – hear the noise of animals
      – it was very dark
E. 1. graceful ; soared
   2. delicious ; exciting
   3. treacherous ; experienced
   4. smashed ; struggled
   5. marathon ; exhausted ; tiredly
   6. chimed ; quaint

2 Clustering Ideas – A Creative Writing Process

A. (Individual writing)
B. (Individual writing)
C. (Individual writing)

3 A Way with Words

A. 1. than 2. weather 3. It's
   4. There 5. threw 6. Whose
   7. sight 8. Quiet 9. lose
   10. wait
B. (Answers may vary.)
   1. I believe dogs make the best pets.
   2. It was an ideal day for sailing.
   3. I think people should eat more fruits and vegetables.
   4. I'm not sure but I think today is her birthday.
   5. I didn't go to the movie because I had already seen it.
   6. I don't understand why some people refuse to exercise.
   7. It was because he was too young to get a job.
C. (Answers will vary.)
   1. The weather report called for sunny skies so they decided to go on a long bike ride. John wanted to try out his new bike that he received as a birthday gift.
   2. John rode a ten-speed bike while Mabel rode a twelve-speed.
   3. Part of their 5-kilometre ride was uphill. At the end they were very tired because they were not used to riding uphill.
   4. The riders stopped for refreshment which made the ride home much easier; they decided to plan another trip for next weekend.
D. 1. My teacher is very good at explaining the Mathematics programme.
   2. The automobile was parked in front of the house for two days.
   3. The pitcher threw a no-hitter.
   4. They looked at the neighbour's pictures of her trip to Europe.
Challenge
   (Answers may vary.)
   1. After she searched throughout the neighbourhood, she found the lost kitten.
   2. The car broke down while they were driving to Ottawa to visit relatives.

4 Writing a Factual Composition

A. (Any 6 of the following)
   (Answers may vary.)
   1. The Asian elephant weighs up to 5,000 kilograms.
   2. The Asian elephant's height is almost 3 metres.
   3. The African elephant weighs 7,000 kilograms.
   4. The African elephant is 4 metres in height.
   5. Tusks are upper incisors.
   6. Incisors continue to grow throughout the life of the elephant.
   7. The elephant's ears have blood vessels that give off heat and cool off the elephant.
   8. Elephants are gentle despite their size.
   9. Elephants live in marshes and river valleys in Southeast Asia, China, and Africa.
   10. Elephants eat up to 300 kilograms of food daily.
   11. Elephants drink up to 190 litres of water.
   12. Elephants have become an endangered species.
   13. Poachers kill elephants for their tusks.
B. (Individual writing)
C. (Individual writing)

5 **Creative Sentence Structure – You're the Architect**

A. (Answers will vary.)
1. They held a barbecue and gave out the awards after the baseball game.
2. The nocturnal animals scurried about deep in the forest beneath the moonlight.
3. She felt embarrassed and her face turned red whenever she gave a speech in front of the class.
4. You should exercise regularly and eat proper food if fitness is important to you.
5. Because his alarm did not go off, he didn't wake up in time.
6. Before the tournament began, the students organized new teams.

B. (Answers may vary.)
1. He delivered newspapers every morning even in bad weather.
2. The airport was crowded with many summer travellers.
3. He saved his money to buy a new eighteen-speed bicycle.
4. When the ice cream truck rang a bell, the children came running out of their houses.

C. (Answers may vary.)
1. He had a good night's sleep; however, he was still tired.
2. Lucy went to a summer camp; therefore, she was gone for two months.
3. Paul arrived early for school; unfortunately, it was Saturday.
4. The elderly lady needed help; sadly, there was no one around.
5. She was chosen the top student; consequently, she received the award.
6. Their team was the best; otherwise, they wouldn't have won.
7. The result was not as expected; nevertheless, they were happy.
8. The cottage was enchanting; truly, it was a special place.

Challenge
(Answer will vary.)
Toronto, Canada's largest city with a population of over 2 million people, is located in Ontario. It is located on Lake Ontario, which is one of the five Great Lakes. Toronto is the most multicultural city in Canada with many people from foreign countries. Toronto is both a banking and manufacturing centre where there are many job opportunities. It is rated in the top ten of the best places to live and work in the world.

6 **Abstract and Concrete Language**

A. 1. A 2. C 3. A 4. C
5. C 6. A 7. C 8. A
9. A 10. A 11. A 12. C
13. A 14. A 15. C 16. C
17. C 18. C 19. C 20. A
B. (Answers will vary.)
C. (Answers will vary.)
Appliances :
1. electric stove 2. steaming iron
3. electric can-opener 4. microwave oven
Food :
1. juicy fruit 2. steaming hot potatoes
3. sizzling bacon 4. creamy peanut butter
Clothing :
1. leather jacket 2. wool sports coat
3. cotton sweater 4. polyester pants
Animals :
1. soaring eagle 2. galloping horse
3. courier pigeon 4. guard dog
The Old House :
1. creaky staircase 2. oak door
3. stained glass windows 4. pine floors
The Seaside :
1. crashing waves 2. hot sand
3. swooping seagulls 4. blazing sunsets
D. 1. family room ; slumped
2. enjoyable ; birthday party ; banquet hall
3. anxious ; water skiing
4. cozy ; quaint
5. clear ; balmy ; ideal
6. intelligent ; response ; debate
7. illuminated ; fans ; cheered

7 **Building Vocabulary (1)**

A. 1. inactive ; activity
2. disability ; able
3. uninterested ; interesting
4. informal ; formalize
5. laughable ; laughter
6. present ; presentable
7. displeasure ; pleasurable
8. occupant ; occupation
B. 1. problem 2. annoy 3. regard
4. create 5. disturb 6. interest
7. credible 8. royal 9. truth
10. colony 11. extinct 12. mischief
13. hope 14. reduce 15. sense
16. delicate 17. regret 18. whole
19. enchant 20. present
C. (Individual answers)

D. 1. difficult 2. shallow
   3. intelligence 4. insulting
   5. abundant 6. annoyed
   7. height 8. all-present

Progress Test 1

A. 1. C 2. E 3. F
   4. A 5. D 6. B
B. 1. B 2. L 3. E 4. I
   5. J 6. K 7. F 8. G
   9. D 10. H 11. A 12. C
C. 1. too ; two ; to 2. than
   3. weather 4. Whether
   5. It's 6. its
   7. Their 8. they're
   9. there 10. threw
   11. threw ; through 12. loose
   13. lose 14. Who's
   15. Whose 16. quit
   17. quiet 18. quite
   19. wait 20. weight
D. 1. I think that exercise is important.
   2. My friend is an excellent student.
   3. It was an important day for him.
   4. I remember that he dropped by last Tuesday.
   5. I don't quite understand how they could walk away from the terrible accident unhurt.
   6. It was a great day for flying kites.
E. (Suggested answers)
   1. The rain poured down and we got soaked.
   2. We laughed at the funny comedian.
   3. We were frightened when the lights went out.
   4. We sold lots of things in a garage sale and made some money.
   5. The bus broke down and we waited a long time for another bus.
   6. The game went into overtime but was tied and there was no winner.
   7. I couldn't be happier to receive a video game from my best friend, Jason, for my birthday and we played it right away.
   8. The lengthy meeting dragged on and on for almost five hours and everybody was bored except the Chairman.
F. (Suggested answers)
   1. It was a rainy day; therefore, the baseball game was cancelled.
   2. I awoke in the middle of the night; however, I was able to get back to sleep shortly afterwards.
   3. We didn't play well; luckily, our captain scored the decisive goal just before the end of the game.
   4. The results were posted; sadly, we did not win.

   5. Their project was the best; otherwise, they wouldn't have won the prize.
G. 1. A 2. A 3. C 4. C
   5. A 6. C 7. C 8. C
   9. C 10. A
H. 1. problem 2. colony 3. reduce
   4. delicate 5. present 6. annoy
   7. consider 8. illusion 9. ordinary
   10. emotion
I. (Suggested answers)
   1a. disagree b. agreeable
   2a. interesting b. disinterested
   3a. presentable b. presenter
   4a. laughing b. laughable
   5a. occupation b. occupant
   6a. disturbing b. disturbance
   7a. displease b. pleasant
   8a. doubtful b. doubtless
   9a. decision b. indecisive
   10a. displace b. misplace

8 Building Vocabulary (2)

A. 1a. ate b. eight
   2a. Sunday b. sundae
   3a. lessen b. lesson
   4a. bear b. bare
   5a. desert b. dessert
   6a. principal b. principle
   7a. paws b. pause
   8a. cent b. scent
   9a. patients b. patience
   10a. jeans b. genes
B. 1. reduce 2. always 3. forget
   4. quick 5. inside 6. final
   7. profit 8. vacant 9. vague
   10. clever 11. compact 12. noisy
C. 1. inflate 2. operate 3. native
   4. please 5. protect 6. chat
   7. analyze 8. count 9. wizardry
   10. prognosis 11. specimen 12. abandon
D. 1. exact ; useful
   2. huge / gigantic ; dwarfed / was much larger than
   3. prediction ; get well
   4. truthful / honest
   5. sleepy / quiet / calm ; slept / lounged / lay about
   6. examined ; example ; type
   7. thought about ; strange
   8. obvious
   9. faithful / true
   10. athletic / coordinated ; move

9 Writing Poetry

A. (Answers will vary.)
1. dome ; home ; foam
2. dog ; frog ; smog
3. play ; way ; tray
4. swipe ; type ; ripe
5. mint ; tint ; flint
6. pop ; drop ; mop
7. duper ; scooper ; trooper
8. sing ; ring ; sting
9. wink ; drink ; sink
10. mood ; glued ; tattooed
11. dock ; flock ; mock
12. blob ; sob ; knob
13. lucks ; trucks ; deducts
14. how ; now ; wow
15. crude ; mood ; sued
16. finer ; minor ; liner
B. (Individual writing)
C. (Individual writing)
D. (Individual writing)

10 Imagery in Poetry

A. (Answers will vary.)
1. infant / boy / girl
2. shark / swordfish / cod
3. rose / daisy / tulip
4. moose / beaver / lion / giraffe
5. goaltender / hockey player
6. trophy / plaque / certificate
7. novel / diary / magazine
8. sweatshirt / cardigan
9. jacket / windbreaker / raincoat
10. spoke / answered / uttered / cried
11. wandered / ventured / strayed
12. struck / hammered / smashed
13. gazed at / viewed / glanced at
14. glad / elated / excited
15. plaything / doll / action figure
16. dog / cat / bird / fish
B. (Answers will vary.)
1. coal
2. a fly
3. morning sunshine
4. a fox
5. a clown
6. a lark
7. straw
8. a star
C. (Answers will vary.)
1. an open book
2. dazzling array of candles
3. wounded animal
4. darts
5. glow
6. bubbles of silk

D. (Answers will vary.)
1. proclaimed
2. rushed
3. bowed its head
4. reached
5. missed
6. waved
7. mimicked
8. stood at attention
9. struggled
10. laughed
11. swam
12. surrounded
E. (Individual writing)

11 Word Origins

A. (Answers may vary.)
1. metre
2. geography
3. telegraph
4. telephone
5. sympathy
6. physical
7. biology
8. philosophy
9. auditorium
10. manual
11. co-operate
12. subscribe
13. judge
14. video
15. beneficial
16. dictation
B. 1. hemisphere
2. monorail
3. century
4. kilometre
5. contradict
6. depart
7. devalue
8. misunderstand
9. forecast
10. postwar
C. 1. kingdom
2. ownership
3. performer
4. competition
5. happiness
6. fatherhood
7. difference
8. compassion
9. competitor
10. circumstance
D. 1. utilize
2. verify
3. negotiate
4. hasten
5. sympathize
6. create
7. simplify
8. loosen
E. 1. fantastic
2. useless
3. partial
4. scrumptious
5. active
6. reliable
7. bashful
8. stylish
F. 1. J
2. E
3. I
4. K
5. L
6. M
7. F
8. N
9. C
10. P
11. B
12. O
13. H
14. G
15. D
16. A

12 Writing Ads and Announcements

A. (Answers will vary.)
1. BIKE FOR SALE
18-speed, 42 cm mountain bike, excellent condition, hardly ridden, extra equipment included. $125.
2. HOUSE FOR RENT
3-bedroom house, near all amenities, yard, garage, finished basement, suits family. $1,400 per month. Oct. 1st.

3. EMPLOYMENT
   Responsible, friendly youth needed for pharmacy delivery in neighbourhood after school and on weekends. Bike provided. $7.25 per hour.
B. (Answer will vary.)
   GARAGE SALE
   Huge garage sale, Sunday, October 11, 9 – 3. Many interesting and useful articles including: fridge, stove, washer, dryer, dining room set, couch and matching chair, coffee table, lamps, carpet, television, stereo, skis, skates, hockey equipment, bicycles, leather coat, men's suits, antique chair, period pieces, art. Everything must go.
C. (Individual writing)
D. (Individual writing)

13 Letter Writing

A. (Individual writing)
B. (Individual writing)
C. (Individual writing)

14 Interviewing Celebrities

A. (Individual writing)
B. 1. less ; fewer   2. laid ; lies
   3. sits ; sets   4. in ; into
   5. May ; Can   6. borrow ; lend
   7. between ; among

15 Preparing to Run a Marathon

A.

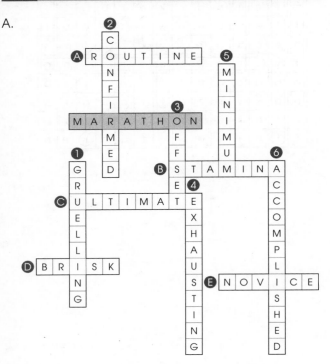

B. (Individual writing)
C. (Individual writing)

Progress Test 2

A. 1. be   2. genes   3. cent
   4. ate   5. weak   6. Sunday
   7. bare   8. lesson   9. guest
   10. desert   11. principle   12. patients
   13. idle   14. paws
B. 1. enlarge   2. seldom   3. remember
   4. vociferous   5. reveal   6. stupid
   7. loss   8. occupied   9. clear
   10. initial   11. core   12. speedy
   13. similar   14. hesitant
C. 1. I   2. E   3. A   4. F
   5. J   6. B   7. K   8. G
   9. C   10. H   11. L   12. D
D. 1. analyzed ; confirm ; type
   2. prognosis ; positive
   3. delighted
   4. disrupted
E. 1. E   2. H   3. F   4. C
   5. G   6. I   7. D   8. J
   9. K   10. B   11. L   12. A
F. 1. metr   2. geo
   3. graph   4. tele
   5. path   6. phys
   7. bio   8. bot
   9. audi   10. manu
   11. op   12. scrib
   13. jur   14. vid
   15. bene   16. dict
G. 1. I   2. F   3. J   4. G
   5. A   6. H   7. B   8. E
   9. C   10. D
H. 1. J   2. I   3. H   4. B
   5. C   6. A   7. F   8. E
   9. G   10. D
I. 1. D   2. H   3. F   4. G
   5. B   6. A   7. C   8. E
J. 1. H   2. E   3. F   4. G
   5. D   6. C   7. B   8. A
K. 1. G   2. H   3. F   4. C
   5. A   6. D   7. B   8. E
L. (Individual writing)

1. (Suggested slides)

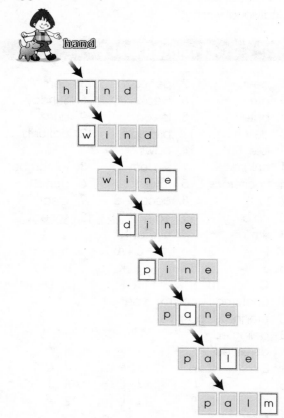

hand

| h | i | n | d |

| w | i | n | d |

| w | i | n | e |

| d | i | n | e |

| p | i | n | e |

| p | a | n | e |

| p | a | l | e |

| p | a | l | m |

2.

dolphin

❶ dolphin

❷ whale

❸ turtle

❹ eel

❺ fish

❻ octopus

3.

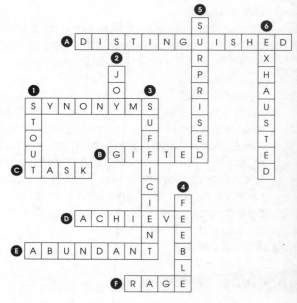

Across / Down

A. DISTINGUISHED
B. GIFTED
C. TASK
D. ACHIEVE
E. ABUNDANT
F. RAGE

Down clues:
1. STOUT
2. JOY
3. SACRIFICE
5. SURPRISE
6. EXHAUSTED
4. FEEBLE

SYNONYMS

4. 1. house (doghouse ; housewife)
   2. work (network ; workshop)
   3. light (starlight ; lighthouse)
   4. bow (rainbow ; bowman)
   5. land (homeland ; landmark)
   6. life (wildlife ; lifetime)

5.

c	i	p	r	k	m	a	h	b	h	i	e	f	o
g	o	a	u	d	e	c	a	n	o	e	i	n	g
n	k	q	v	h	r	l	d	i	c	c	g	b	p
b	b	a	s	e	b	a	l	l	k	r	u	n	c
a	v	j	w	g	y	c	z	x	e	m	t	s	y
d	o	l	i	j	k	i	t	b	y	v	s	d	c
m	l	c	m	b	a	s	k	e	t	b	a	l	l
i	l	e	m	o	e	n	w	v	n	y	c	p	i
n	e	o	i	a	r	s	g	k	z	n	t	m	n
t	y	s	n	o	w	b	o	a	r	d	i	n	g
o	b	d	g	o	v	j	l	c	w	x	y	s	b
n	a	s	y	s	z	d	f	l	c	u	a	f	g
b	l	h	k	q	t	n	c	x	d	e	r	t	p
f	l	b	j	l	e	w	u	f	q	c	r	m	h

6. (Suggested slides)

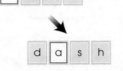 fish

d i s h

d a s h

l a s h

l a s t

l o s t

l o s e

l o v e

8.

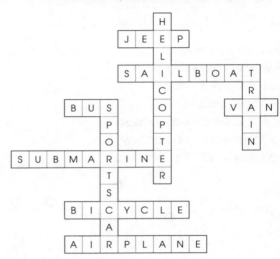

9.

10. (Suggested answers)

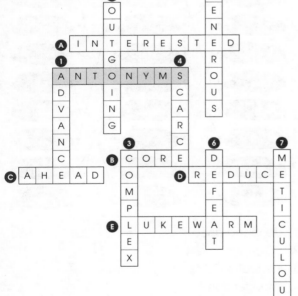

7.

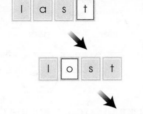

11.

E	N	S	A	T	O	N	E	M	E	R	N	T	O
S	C	P	L	I	E	P	A	A	C	X	M	Y	W
B	U	T	U	K	Y	M	E	R	F	W	I	S	H
R	Y	C	R	V	E	N	U	S	N	E	P	R	E
A	R	T	A	P	B	I	J	A	U	S	K	Y	D
U	P	T	N	O	C	L	A	M	E	U	P	I	E
R	T	M	U	E	Q	C	R	U	T	N	V	R	A
A	O	C	S	Y	P	R	A	J	U	R	E	S	P
P	L	A	R	O	Z	T	X	N	E	A	R	T	H
S	A	T	U	R	N	H	U	T	E	R	S	T	V
K	M	D	I	S	J	U	I	N	U	E	T	Y	E
M	U	S	R	A	F	P	O	I	E	O	H	P	N
E	M	E	R	C	U	R	Y	L	Q	M	S	E	O
S	U	B	G	J	V	A	N	R	D	O	K	U	R
O	Z	Q	I	M	E	P	T	H	U	E	D	S	Y
T	S	A	T	H	R	E	A	C	I	M	W	O	P

12. (Suggested answers)
   1-syllable word – sing
   2-syllable word – carry
   3-syllable word – justify
   4-syllable word – comfortable
   5-syllable word – characteristic
   6-syllable word – internationally

13.

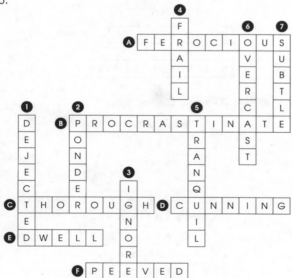

14.

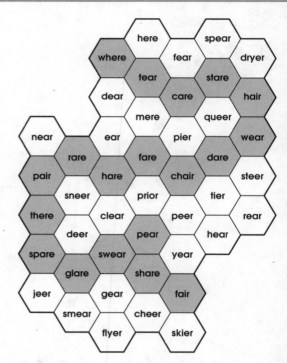

15. (Individual colouring of the rhyming pairs)
   tower – sour
   brief – leaf
   caught – bought
   halt – salt
   soar – pour

16.

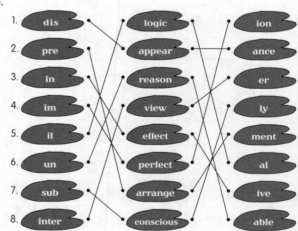

1. disappearance
2. prearrangement
3. ineffective
4. imperfection
5. illogical
6. unreasonable
7. subconsciously
8. interviewer

ISBN: 978-1-897457-06-1